THE BOY OF WILNA
Copyright 1941, by Hebrew Publishing Co.

To
MAJOR LEON GINSBURG
Surgeon and Humanitarian

*Set up by Hebrew Publishing Co., New York
Printed in the United States of America.*

Elijah ben Solomon was born in or near Wilna in 1720, and died there in 1797. He is known as the Gaon of Wilna—the title Gaon (meaning "Excellency) here implies genius, and leadership in learning and judgment. It is said of him that he could read an entire book and recall every word in it. Not alone was he the master of all Jewish learning, but he was noteworthy for his knowledge of mathematics and science. Thus, to treatises and commentaries covering all biblical, talmudic, and rabbinical lore he added others on algebra, geometry, and astronomy. He could in a moment decide a question that troubled other scholars for weeks. Elijah opposed the Jewish sect which glorified devotion without learning. Though we know very little about his life, we are acquainted with his brilliant mind and saintly character; and we know just what sort of life all Jews lived in Lithuania at the period covered by this story.

1

Elijah Talks

The thin man with the scraggy beard threw his head back so forcefully that a series of ripples glided down his greenish-black gabardine. He placed each foot between rounded cobblestones, and then held up a commanding hand.

"It is not possible !" he cried, looking balefully at no person present, though he was addressing three younger men in the city square. "They can say what they want to you, but Ezekiel Batlan cannot be fooled !"

"Ezekiel Batlan has been fooled more than once !" sneered one of the others. "He is no oracle !"

The argumentative Ezekiel slid his head forward on his shoulders until it took its normal hanging position, but his eyes flashed.

"So !" he shrieked. "All at once I know nothing ! You young idiots are telling me ! Me, who prophecied that Charles of Sweden would take this city in 1708, and who lived through the pestilence and the persecution ! Me, who nine times out of ten predicted whether a boy or a girl would be born in the leading families of Wilna ! Me — "

"Wrong !" broke in the other. "It was three times out of ten. The rest of the time you guessed after you heard the news !"

Ezekiel Batlan grew doubly red and irate.

"That I should live to be publicly insulted like this! But what difference does it make ? After all, whom am I talking to? Do they know what they are saying? I say again — no boy can deliver a homily to a congregation at seven years old. Maybe he is clever enough to learn by heart what his father Solomon tells him. Somebody can stand nearby to prompt him. But speak on his own account? This was never before heard of in Israel!"

"Let us go, Simon," urged another of the three listeners to the first speaker.

But the third, who had been looking around the square, nudged Simon with a tattered elbow.

"Wait, Simon," he said. "Wait, Reuben. Let him talk. Some one is coming."

Ezekiel, still in possession of an audience, resumed his oration. He spoke loudly, evidently hoping to enlarge the number of listeners. Then a strange thing happened. His mouth, opened to shout a good round vowel, became paralyzed. No sound issued; the jaws would not move. Advancing, or rather waddling, upon him was a short round female with a sharp nose that belied the rotundity of her other features. She pushed her way through the onlookers and wiggled a finger almost between the frightened Ezekiel's teeth.

"Filthy one!" she screamed. "Talkative ignoramus! Great man that you think you are! Making speeches while I push the vegetable cart! If I killed you now kings and judges would forgive me and praise me. What good are you in the world altogether?"

Ezekiel's mouth had gradually resumed its ordinary contour. He turned as to flee, but an augmented and

8

happy crowd blocked him in every direction. He spluttered fearsomely.

"Please, Shprintze! Not in the street! Must you carry on household quarrels before all Wilna? Must you—"

But Shprintze reached up an agile arm, caught the ear of her errant husband, and dragged him through the delighted group with a new stream of invective. In hardly a moment he was between the shafts of a two wheeled cart, sweating both from the exertion of pushing and from the fear of further verbal assault.

But there was another intrusion into the group that watched the conjugal encounter. Two large ruffians, obviously not Jews, clad in bulgy round cloth caps, brown leather coats that hung a foot below the waist, rough wool breeches, and oversize boots, stationed themselves in the center of the ring of men. They might have been members of some uniformed company, with their similar accoutrements; and their faces, though quite dissimilar, were alike in that their noses sprawled unprettily over their cheeks.

The Jews made no effort to escape. No one spoke. Even if these *goyim* intended to attack them, they had no open weapons, and could be overcome by numbers. But there was fear in every glance.

One of the newcomers, noting the hostility they had evoked, essayed a grisly smile. He too held up his hand.

"Now, now," he spoke. "I am Stasz, and this is my friend Vanoff. We are travelers, and want to see everything that is interesting in every city. That is why we stepped in here. We heard this man who went away talking about something that is impossible, something

9

about a child seven years old. All we want is information, so that we can look at the marvel too before we start off to Bopt."

The second interloper also smiled ingratiatingly, and both bowed as though in deference to the assembled congregation.

The man called Simon offered to explain.

"It is this. We have here in Wilna a brilliant young student, named Elijah ben Solomon. The boy is so far advanced in his studies that his teachers have asked him to deliver the Sabbath sermon in the great synagogue. And this dolt Ezekiel, with the shrewish wife, plants himself in the middle of the square and says it is impossible!"

"And is it all true what they say about the boy?" asked Stasz, simulating more interest.

"Of course it is true! His father is a great scholar; I know him. He taught the boy when he was practically an infant. And whereas most boys are able to study the Jewish books by themselves when they are ten or older, this little Elijah dispensed with a teacher when he was six!"

The rough intruders threw up their hands in wonder, and smiled broadly as though by a prearranged signal.

"Well," suggested the one called Vanoff, "if this Solomon can take the time from his business to teach children, he must be well-off."

There was a sudden silence among the Jewish group. However, Reuben spoke up quickly, evidently without thought of his words.

"Solomon is one of the richest Jews in Wilna!" he

declared. "He is a scholar, a leader, an ornament to Judaism!"

Simon struck his talkative friend sharply in the side. Reuben at once grew pale. The group disappeared as though by magic, leaving the interrogators alone in the square. These two turned to each other and laughed.

Their mirth must have reached the ears of the three young men who had first hearkened to Ezekiel Batlan's doubts.

"Dolt!" Simon addressed his friend Reuben. "Did I say anything? Did Asher speak? Everybody was silent, but you. Why did these *goyim* ask that last question? Burglars, kidnapers, murderers—are only interested in ways to rob Jews. And you had to tell them Solomon is rich. You had to give them ideas. Next time when a stranger asks you, say the man is poor; say he has nothing. Through you an evil eye has fallen upon Solomon—and upon his son Elijah!"

Reuben, almost tearful, plodded along without a word. He knew how dangerous it was to tell a certain type of non-Jewish stranger what any Jew's circumstances were. There had been burglaries and worse, committed by malefactors who sojourned in Wilna only long enough to plot and execute a crime against its Jewish citizenry. They disappeared at once. There seldom was redress; and there rarely was a police official who worried greatly over the outrage an hour after the report had been rendered.

What worried Simon most was that these gentile strangers had understood and spoken Yiddish, the language employed by practically all Wilna Jews. This was an indication that they were clever men, who would not hesitate to pass themselves off as Jews if they in truth had come to Wilna with nefarious purposes. Many a calamity had befallen the local Jewry in days past through aliens who had, with a smattering of Jewish knowledge, insinuated themselves into the community.

It was Friday. Stasz and Vanoff, happy in the possession of valuable information, entered a Jewish inn and ordered liquor. The proprietor, a tall Jew named Paltiel, at first was reluctant to entertain these unprepossessing strangers, but he was partly reassured when the men spoke in fluent Yiddish. They paid promptly, after each round, and the innkeeper gradually thawed out. Stasz, waiting for just this opportunity, casually mentioned the fame of little Elijah ben Solomon. Paltiel took the bait, and soon rapidly sketched the career of the lad, and went on to describe the father's benefactions and his fine home, a stone's throw from the great synagogue.

No sooner had this added information been given them than the two rose, nodded, and quickly proceeded on their way. Paltiel looked after them, jingled his coins, and turned to several new customers who had just entered.

From this establishment Stasz and Vanoff hied to another hostelry conducted by a Pole called Peter Peter, after a double sign that swung above the hinges. Here they were more at home, for Peter Peter—as we shall again term him this once—grinned hospitably as they entered.

"Well?" he inquired. "Any luck?"

"Not yet," Stasz grinned back." But another day or two—you'll see."

"A Jew?"

"Naturally. Get us some supper. We'll tell you more later."

When the two departed on the morrow, they beheld an unusual multitude of Jewish citizens making their way to the great synagogue. Mingling with the rest, they were able to reach a corner bench, and there, with prayershawls and books, give the impression of being regular members of the congregation.

They rose and sat with all the worshipers, mumbling words that might be taken for the sacred Hebrew they knew nothing of. The regular morning service was repeated by the cantor; the scroll was taken from the Ark and read by a procession of grown Jews called up for that purpose; and finally, with the related prophetic portion recited, the ceremony of returning the scroll was completed. There was a moment of rustling as all the congregants, including the women in the completely hidden galleries, took their seats.

The synagogue was a lofty structure, with huge stone pillars supporting the roof on decorative arches. The reading desk was backed by three smaller arches, and one above; a short stairway led to the repository of the scrolls. Wooden benches, with reading attachments, faced toward the middle line of the structure. From many points in the building one could not see the cantor or the preacher; but their voices were easily carried into every cranny. This was the case with the women's balcony, from whose curtained privacy no feminine worshiper ever dared to look down.

But now necks were being craned from every seat. As Solomon, the respected communal leader, arose, he

13

bowed to both sides, where sat a group of visiting scholars and rabbis. Then he proceeded at once to his task.

"Honored congregation," he began, "today it is my pleasure to do that which has been the ambition of every father and mother in Israel since children have been taught the sacred lore of our people. We all wish our youth to study and understand and expound the Law; and so have I too tried to teach my firstborn the lessons of the past. But God has been good to me, and given me a child who no longer needs my assistance in learning. It was not at my request that the boy was asked to speak here today; I would not dare to make such a petition for one who is but seven years of age. But these men of learning whom you see here before me—they have been good enough to praise my son and to suggest that he speak the homily at this service. I humbly thank God for having given me so gifted a lad; and I am grateful to the officials of the Jewish community for having provided this opportunity to start him on a career of learning and teaching. Please be so good as to remember that he is a little boy; and if he stops or stumbles, pardon him. Men of the Wilna community, I entrust my son to your judgment!"

There was a murmur in the galleries, punctuated by exclamations of delight and endearment. For the little one, small for his age, and dressed in blue silk garments somewhat like a sailor suit of today, had come to his father's side like a doll propelled by some mechanism. He stood there straight and unafraid, seemingly an accomplished orator.

Two officials placed a box support behind the prea-

14

cher's stand, and the boy Elijah put his little hands over the side of the stand exactly as he had seen rabbis do on the Sabbaths marked by preaching. Then in a voice clear and surprisingly strong, he quoted his text and outlined the talmudic elaborations on the biblical words. It was a simple homily, urging Israel to observe the laws of the Sabbath by describing its importance to God and Israel, and mentioning the need and value of rest from the world's material things. For twenty minutes the childish voice continued, employing no notes or reminders of any kind, and proceeding as smoothly as a well rehearsed theatre piece.

When Elijah had ended, he turned, was helped off his support by the officials, and then stood up by the side of his father. Solomon, overcome, reached down as though to lift the lad in his arms, but quickly the cantor began the doxology preliminary to the additional Sabbath prayer and he straightened up. The boy too recited this prayer, for which all stood; and he rose again as the cantor repeated the holier portions of the services. None spoke until the worship was completely ended, and then there was a hubbub such as had never before been heard in the synagogue's history.

Women screamed words of love and admiration from their place above. Men and boys fought to reach Solomon, to congratulate him while wishing both a good Sabbath. Elijah, his eyes open with astonishment, for to him what he had said was simply a more public exposition of his lessons, clung to his father's hand.

At length most of the congregants had gone through the doors, leaving the edifice to those in the front center benches. The visiting rabbis were conversing excitedly.

16

"Such genius must be fostered!" exclaimed one.

"Can he be left in Wilna for that?" inquired another.

"No, no!" came the general exclamation. "We must find him the wisest teacher in Europe!"

"You have a wonder child, Master Solomon!" rose one voice, that of a young man with a fringe of black beard indicating his recent emergence from youth. "You should send him to the best schools and masters."

Solomon looked bewildered.

"You gentlemen are agreed that my son must be taken from me!" he protested.

"But we cannot allow genius to be neglected," responded the bearded young man. "I am Rabbi Abraham Katzenellenbogen of Brest-Litovsk, or Brisk, as it is better known. My father is Rabbi of Kaidan, as you know—his name is David. And he will be glad to find the proper teacher for this boy."

"He is so young!" protested Solomon. "How can we take him from his mother at this age? And,'" he added, with a sigh, "from his father? Must I sacrifice so much for his education?"

"You have a choice," earnestly pleaded the rabbi, "and yet you have no choice. Learning to us is equivalent to all other virtues. From what I have heard today, I am convinced that this lad is one in a generation, perhaps one in a century. Israel needs such as him. You and your wife love this boy, but you love Israel too. And would not any parent offer sacrifices to assure a son of permanent fame?"

The little Elijah said nothing. Still practically a baby, he was only distinguished when employed in scholarly pursuits. Otherwise he clung to his father's hand and in his heart knew that he would obey his parents in any matter that might be discussed and in which he was concerned. Solomon several times looked down fondly on his offspring, sighed each time, and then turned to the rabbi.

"You would take good care of him?" he said.

"As my own! In my father's own home. You would be able to travel to see him at times; perhaps before holidays travelers will be able to take him to you. Give me your answer."

"As you present the case," breathed Solomon, "I have no answer. I cannot refuse the opportunity for my little one. But we must prepare his mother too. She will take it hard. Only yesterday he was in the cradle. Every moment of the time she will be worrying—whether his bed is comfortable, or his food is well prepared, or if he is ill, or perhaps lest he forget his loving family in distant places."

The other rabbis joined in urging that Elijah be granted the most advantageous educational opportunities. So long did they talk that when they departed from the synagogue, the congregation had dispersed for the Sabbath meal. Their desire to congratulate the precocious youth could not hold against the pull of appetite. A number of the visitors joined Solomon and Elijah, for they were dinner guests in the home of the communal leader.

During the short walk to his home Solomon spoke no word. He held tightly to Elijah's hand, revolving in his mind the arguments that would have to be presented to the mother at the conclusion of the Sabbath.

It was only after all attendants at the service had

disappeared into their homes that two grinning interlopers, who had been sprawled behind a bench during
all the colloquy in the synagogue, cautiously unbarred
the door and walked out into the street.

"We know what the boy looks like," said Stasz.

"And his father looks like a man who would not stint
on ransom money," added Vanoff. "He would give every
groschen he has for that boy."

"Did you hear what that rabbi from Brisk said?" continued Stasz. "You know the road. If this thing goes
through, we are prepared for a killing without the least
danger."

"Keep your eyes open. When they start out, we go
along. Stasz, we are rich already!"

Upon which Vanoff laughingly began counting in
Yiddish the thousands that the projected kidnaping
would bring them both.

19

2

The Journey

The tears shed during the ensuing days over little Elijah were not alone induced by the prospect of his departure. Nor were the possible hardships he would suffer in strange cities entirely involved. For in those days and in those lands no traveler was ever secure. Highwaymen roamed the narrow dirt roads over which carts and carriages jolted. Many inns were not safe for the wayfarer. In the dusk the driver might inadvertently turn off into the forest, with its additional perils.

Jews in particular were liable to assault. Merchants, as many of them were, could be expected to carry full purses. The people of Israel were notoriously susceptible to demands for ransom. All this the family of Elijah knew.

It was arranged, however, that the party containing the lad travel by the main roads, leading southwesterly toward Warsaw through Grodno and Bialystok. At the latter city, a turn to the southeast would bring the voyagers through well populated country into Brest-Litovsk.

The boy Elijah, clutching a little bundle of extra garments, tried hard to restrain the tears that persisted in filling his eyes. His parents, themselves openly weeping, had insisted that he must be brave, as he was going on the path of glory, to the greater honoring of the Lord.

They had repeated that learning was the greatest of *mitzvot,* of religious commands.

Next to him in the carriage sat Rabbi Abraham. Katzenellenbogen, he of the long name and the large intellect. The seats opposite them were occupied by a newly wed pair. The bride, leaving home to be with her husband, alternately wept and laughed as she contemplated her new life or regretted the loss of the old. They were too preoccupied to pay much attention to the rabbi and the little boy.

The roof of the closed conveyance was piled with bedclothes and other parts of the bride's dowry, leaving hardly an inch for the carpet roll in which the rabbi carried his major effects. On the driver's seat sat a grizzled veteran of the road, accompanied by a bodyguard armed with a very large pistol. The scenery was drab and flat, though the summer had just begun. There was a threat of rain in the air.

The rabbi patted the boy's hand.

"We shall see some very fine cities," he comforted. "There are many interesting places outside of Wilna."

"But Wilna," soberly replied the precocious child, "is where I was born, and where my father and mother are."

"You will see them often," returned the rabbi. "They will come to you or you will come to them. In the mean while, my father will care for you in a good home. He will find the right teacher for you, and you will become a great scholar."

"Couldn't I become a scholar in Wilna?"

"You know that there are not many first class teachers in the world, and unfortunately the most cap-

Sol Nadel

able of them are not in your city. You need special attention; you are different."

These words cheered the youngster. If he were in truth different, it would be unseemly for him further to protest his transfer to distant parts. His was a special destiny. He could be a man even at seven.

They stopped at a Jewish inn for refreshment. This was not far out of the city; the proprietor knew Solomon and had heard of the achievement of his son in the synagogue. He offered the travelers some advice.

"Be careful where you go, and do not cover too much in a day. Arrange to stay at Jewish inns even if there are two more hours of daylight left to travel in. I can give you a list of them, and the distances between. Look out for strangers on horseback, if there are more than one."

It was during the next hour following their departure from this wayside spot that Elijah, looking out the side of the conveyance, saw three horsemen silhouetted on a distant hill. As they rolled through the valleys the men could not be seen, and the boy forgot about them for the time. In half an hour the carriage was approaching the crest of the highest hill, when as though magically three riders appeared before the coach and pointed pistols at the driver and his guard. The guard did make a futile effort to draw his weapon from its holster, but he was too late. The travelers held their arms in the air, while the sharply halted horses snorted in fright.

"Come out!" shouted the leader in Polish.

The white faced bridegroom stepped out, followed by his faltering wife. Elijah, not yet fully aware of the criminal drama about to be enacted, stood for a moment on the upper step. The rabbi looked over his shoulder, one hand on the boy's head.

Before the highwaymen could complete their purpose, however, two additional horsemen, who had evidentaly also been following the carriage, rode madly up and pointed their pistols at the heads of the two men who had taken their places at the sides.

"Turn about!" cried the newcomers. And the men who were covered, seeing it useless to attempt to fight it out from their position, quickly faced forward. The third man, in front, made a gesture as though to fire, but his accomplices were now directly in line before the avengers. He too shrugged his shoulders, and turned forward.

"Get on your horses!" now commanded one of the rescuing pair.

The three silently complied.

"Now get along before—"

But the highwaymen had already spurred forward, and were soon lost down the road. Somewhat shakily the passengers turned to the carriage door. Recalling what the Jewish innkeeper had told them, they were hardly reassured by the appearance of the rescuers.

One of the men approached, however, hat in hand, and bowing with all the grace of a gorilla.

"My name," he began, "is Stasz. This is Vanoff." The other smirked. "We come from Wilna—that is, we were in Wilna when this lad spoke at the synagogue. We are happy that we could do him and you all a service."

27

The guard on the driver's seat scowled and tightened his grip on his pistol. The man called Vanoff at once raised his own weapon half way, only to lower his arm as Stasz kicked at him. The boy Elijah, standing in front of the party, was the only one to notice the gesture.

Stasz knew that he would have to make stronger efforts to win over the doubting company. He spoke again.

"You need not fear us," he protested. "Vanoff and I are not highwaymen. We carry arms only for protection on the road. Drive on; and if we see those men again, we shall not let them off so easily!"

The passengers resumed their seats. While the three adults still shook with fear, Elijah seemed quite pleased by the adventure. Locked up with his books almost from a moment he could toddle, he had sometimes felt the need of a more playful, romantic existence. The journey now took on the aspects of life which perpetual study would never allow him.

The rabbi marveled at the placidity of the child.

"One cannot say," he pondered, "that the lad did not understand what was going on. He is too intelligent. Perhaps he is lacking in fear. But I must not be less calm that he is."

Quickly reassuring himself, the rabbi sat back as though nothing untoward had occurred. The newlyweds held each other closely, still pale with fright. The driver flicked his whip over the horse. Now the guard placed the pistol over his knee, prepared to shoot if necessary without delay.

Then the bridegroom spoke.

"At any rate," he solaced the young woman at his side, "it cannot happen more than once on a journey. We are safe now."

"I hope so," she replied. "But somehow every jolt of the carriage now seems like a blow from a robber."

"Fright does make a person sensitive," interposed Rabbi Katzenellenbogen. "See how composed we are—myself and the boy. Do not permit the incident to spoil your happiness."

The bride nodded dumbly, leaned her head on her husband's shoulder, and closed her eyes. The rabbi himself leaned on the cushioned back of the seat, to give further impression of indifference to dangers past or imminent. Only Elijah, saying nothing of his suspicions, looked back through the window on occasion and nodded.

Thus they traveled as far as Grodno without incident. Near this town there were a number of hostelries owned by Jews, and they felt perfectly secure. But after they had eaten a midday meal at an inn just south of the town, Elijah addressed his companions.

"Every innkeeper," he said, "tells us the same thing —to look out for robbers on horseback."

"Do not fear, child," rejoined the bridegroom. "It cannot happen again to us."

"So you said before," somewhat pettishly protested the bride. "Yet everyone warns us everywhere we go."

"Let us not quarrel," pleaded the young man. "We have just been married."

"You'll begin sooner or later," interposed the driver, who had been listening from a nearby table. "Now, me and my wife—"

29

"Oh, shut your mouth!" cried the guard. "Let them find out for themselves!"

The young married pair both became silent, looking doubtfully at the other table and at each other. The rabbi smiled, and took up the discussion.

"Let us hear from the boy," he said. "He did not finish what he began. What are you thinking of, Elijah?"

The child spoke without hesitation.

"Since everyone warns us about robbers, and since one guard is not enough"—their own guard looked up sheepishly—"why cannot we travel with other coaches for protection?"

The rabbi nodded appreciatively.

"A simple precaution," he commented, " and none of us thought of it. Only this seven-year-old, this infant!"

"But where are we to find other coaches, at this moment?" demanded the driver.

"I was looking back—for something," answered Elijah, "and I saw two carriages come out of the side roads after we had passed. I think if we wait here long enough they will catch up with us."

And that is what happened. Just as the diners were finishing their tea, an equipage drew up before the inn and a half dozen bearded Jews entered. They were merchants from Suwalki, with two armed drivers. One of them knew Rabbi Katzenellenbogen, and soon both companies were fraternizing in the greatest of amity. The newly arrived party had met no felons on their way, and this may have been explained by the fact that each driver displayed not one but two pistols, and assured the curious lad that he could shoot equally well with either hand.

The next load of travelers was from Marienpol—a mother and three children, with an unarmed coachman.

The rabbi broached the proposition of his young charge, but not before he had explained the boy's extraordinary talents. The men of the first coach were more impressed with the opportunity of riding in the company of a young genius than that of combining for the general protection. And the unprotected occupants of the third vehicle were highly pleased with the security of the new arrangement.

When all had eaten they resumed their journey, the family group in the center, and the six longbeards in the rear. Thus, along stretches of dust, Elijah's party had all the advantages. The children in the next coach would come into each stopping place coughing and demanding water. It was then decided that a quarter mile should separate the carriages, permitting the dust raised by the previous riders to settle.

Through Bialystok they proceeded, a happy caravan for those days, when travel implied many of the hardships later to be undergone by the American covered wagons. But there was no journeying along grassy prairies in Poland of the early eighteenth century; either one was smothered with dust or mired in mud. Nothing other was to be expected, however; hence the hardships of the journey were not greatly felt.

In the inns the travelers busied themselves not alone with their own needs, but formed themselves into a protectorate for the three children and their harassed mother. These were returning from a trip to distant grandparents; the husband and father was a dealer in grain some miles north of Brest-Litovsk. The occupants of the larger coach were going beyond the city on a deal in certain precious goods, most probably gems, which could readily be transported without detection by men of the road.

Despite the apparent safety in which they were proceeding, Elijah was still considering the incident of the two sets of horsemen. At one stop he made it a point to address the guard, who, having noted the deference with which the tiny scholar was being treated, was honored by the attention.

"Did you ever shoot that pistol?" he inquired.

"Many times," replied the guard. "I have driven off at least a hundred robbers with it. Sometimes," he added, ruefully, "I fail—when they come upon me before I can draw. But I assure you, master, it will never happen again!"

"I think," declared the lad, "I can help you."

"You help me!" laughed the man. "You are too small. And besides, now that we are traveling in three, there is no more danger."

"But," urged Elijah, "we are not traveling close together; we may be separated, and someone may rob us on a bend in the road."

"And what is your idea, lad?"

"You tie a small rope to your pistol arm so that it will hang near the window. I'll keep a lookout to the rear and side, and if there is any danger I'll pull the rope."

"And what do I do then?"

"Discharge the pistol and scare off the robbers!"

Somewhat doubtfully, but with full recognition of the boy's reputed wisdom, the guard complied with this plan. Some distance out of Brest-Litovsk the coach containing the little family, having reached its destination, dropped out of the procession. One of the drivers of the other escorting coach spoke to the rabbi.

"It is all safe now," he asserted. "We are very near the city, and the roads are generally full. We are in a hurry, so please exuse us if we go ahead."

Elijah's driver nodded assent, and soon they were again alone on the highway. They met people plodding along the roadside, but no wagons except peasants' carts. The boy was wide awake, while his fellow passengers were making futile efforts to dose in the jolting conveyance. Still troubled, he would glance backward and to the side every moment or two, and then cup his ears to catch any untoward sound.

Then he heard it. The muffled neigh of a horse coming from a bend in the highway. He imagined too that he could distinguish additional hoofbeats over those of the carriage horses. His eyes strained toward the shrubbery at the bend, and then he seized the rope end dangling by the window.

Just as they started to turn, he tugged violently. The guard, who had indeed been drowsing, jerked his arm suddenly, pulled the trigger, and discharged the pistol with a roar that echoed from the nearby forest. The horses reared up, just as two other steeds, frightened by the report, dashed by the halted carriage.

The driver and guard leaped from their perch, the latter brandishing his weapon fiercely.

"These are the men!" cried Elijah, from within.

33

"The same who pretended to save us from the three others near home! They are robbers too!"

The guard scratched his head, then reached over to pat Elijah's.

"You're a smart lad," he declared, projecting his lower lip with emphasis. "You must be a prophet, knowing what was going to happen, and making me shoot."

Rabbi Katzenellenbogen leaped from the carriage, and was told of the scheme devised by Elijah.

"But why," he mused aloud, "did these fellows pursue us all the way from Wilna? None of us has much money. Perhaps—perhaps—"

He looked suddenly toward Elijah, and his face sank.

"Driver," he called, "hurry into the city as fast as you can go! It is not far! I think these men are not ordinary robbers, but kidnapers!"

No more dreaded word could have been uttered by the perturbed rabbi. Kidnapers were accustomed to hold Jews, especially little children, for high ransom on pain of death to the victims; and more often than not they killed their captives even after ransom had been paid.

When the carriage finally reached the inhabited outskirts of the city the mouths of the weary horses were lathered with foam.

3

Lonesome Boy

The last miles of the journey were along the great Bug river, which flows through the middle of Poland until it reaches the Vistula, somewhat north of Warsaw. Small boats moved in the middle of the stream, all apparently going down toward the sea.

The carriage containing Elijah seemed to swim in a sea of dust, so eager was the driver to reach inhabited land before new adventures overtook them. The boy wished to contemplate the cool scenery of the water-front, to look at birds and reeds and people—everything odd or striking in a strange land. But there was no slowing up until they came to the arched bridge over the River Mukowetz, which joined the Bug directly north of the city. Then the coach horses were permitted to cross at their leisure.

Once on the other side, the driver unharnessed the foaming animals and allowed them to drink at the river brink. The passengers looked enviously at the weary steeds, hoping that some cool fountain fit for human use might be immediately visible. The dust irritated their skins and discolored their clothes.

The driver, aided by the guard, then coolly proceeded to wash off the coach, using two wooden buckets that had been strung up behind. The passengers became impatient.

"We are thirsty," complained Rabbi Katzenellenbogen. "Why don't you go directly into the city?"

The driver turned a look of displeasure on the rabbi.

"Don't you want to look your best when you come
to a strange place?" he asked. "I want my carriage to
be presentable too!"

"None of us look proper," was the rejoinder. "Only
the wood and metal will be clean when we arrive."

"You people can go into a house to wash," replied
the driver, tossing another bucketful against the sides,
"but you can't do that with horses and conveyance."

Here Elijah stepped forward.

"Though we cannot drink the river wather," he said,
"let us at least throw some over our dusty faces."

At once the four travelers reached for the bucket
just filled by the guard and splashed its contents over
their features, thus gaining relief and renewed good
humor. The horses, now stepping slowly over a stony
roadway, passed a number of widely separated houses
before reaching the first small city settlement. In another
moment the bridegroom spoke up.

"You will find my street directly to the left. Please
turn in."

"Certainly," returned the driver. "I would not leave
you with your belongings in the middle of the road."

On the sideroad, whose dusty smoothness attested
to the rarity of travel thereon, they saw a dozen small
wooden homes in a semi-circular arrangement. At the
suggestion of the bridegroom, who now remembered
to tell the others that he was called Mordecai and his
wife Esther—an unusual biblical coincidence—the driver

swerved to the rear and halted on a pleasant expanse of grass.

"We are home, Estherel!" cried the husband.

"It is lovely!" beamed the bride, who had never lived so close to nature's greenery.

The rabbi and Elijah stepped down to permit Mordecai to carry his young wife across the sward to their new home. Suddenly, from another house there was a wild shout, and a lad of ten bounded from the steps on which he seemed to have been watching, catapulting himself against the pair with such violence as to deposit both on the ground. But Mordecai was not disturbed. He rose, raised Esther up with him, and embraced the lad with shouts of endearment.

"My only brother! My little brother!" he explained to his bride. "He is staying with neighbors till the family returns from the wedding feast."

"Where are papa and mama?" cried the little one.

"They will be here tomorrow, Asher," said Mordecai. "We went ahead."

Everyone, even the tiny Elijah, helped to unload the parcels brought from Wilna by the newlyweds. Rolls of bedding, pots and pans, and a bundle of books all covered with dust, were taken from the coach, permitting the springs to sigh with rusty relief. The boys, who preferred to carry the books in ones or twos rather than the more oppressive bundles, became quickly familiar.

"Are you coming to live here?" asked Asher.

"Yes," replied Elijah. "I am here to study."

"To study?" Asher seemed mystified. "Haven't you any Talmud Torahs in Wilna?"

"We have, but my father wants me to study more advanced work."

Here Mordecai bent down and whispered into Asher's ear.

"But," was the boy's loud response, "he's even littler than me!"

Mordecai whispered again, and Asher nodded, very gravely.

"Listen," he turned to Elijah; "can you help me sometimes in my Hebrew studies? I go to the Talmud Torah here."

"I am not sure whether I know more than you," said Elijah, modestly.

"Oh, yes, you do! They told me."

Here the rabbi interposed.

"If Elijah has time from his regular studies, he'll be glad to study with you, Asher. But now we are going to my house."

Asher took the hand of the young rabbi, whom he had frequently seen about the Hebrew school.

"Let me go along, will you? I never have a chance to ride behind horses."

The rabbi looked toward Mordecai, who nodded.

"All right," he said. "It is a very short ride, but if the driver has no objection, neither have I."

Asher piled in happily after the two remaining passengers; the driver swung the horses around, and shortly they were riding up to the more imposing home of Rabbi Abraham Katzenellenbogen.

The rabbi's mother, wife of Rabbi David Katzenellenbogen of Kaidan, came forth to greet the newcomers.

She kissed her son, and then turned smilingly to the boys.

"Two of them?" she cried. "Oh, no, this is our own little Asher. Then you are the famous Elijah we have all heard about!"

She embraced the child. But Elijah, remembering his own mother and her tears as he departed, felt his eyes growing moist. Despite every exhortation by his loved ones to be brave in his new environment, he was unable to control himself, and soon the *rebbetzin* was wiping away his tears and offering him comfort. Even Asher felt like weeping when he saw this handsome little lad mourning for his distant parents. He took the hand of his new found friend, who smiled gratefully.

The younger rabbi remained without, to offer gratuities to the driver and guard, who then went to the rear of the house to wash and to be given food and drink by the kitchen maid. Both boys accompanied the *rebbetzin* to her husband's study.

This was a somewhat gloomy roon, lined with huge tomes, all covered in mottled yellow leather. At a table near the window sat the Rabbi of Kaidan, temporarily officiating for his son, his eyes so closely bent over a book that he knew naught of the approach of visitors.

"Rabbi!" called his wife.

He started and looked up with wide eyes.

"What it is, my dear?" he demanded.

"Look down here," she returned. "Here is our little honored guest."

The rabbi squinted in the direction indicated, and suddenly his face lit up.

39

"The boy of Wilna!" he cried. "The child they have been telling us about! You are welcome here!"

Elijah's little hand was timidly placed in the large hairy hand of the rabbi, who seemed overcome with happiness to look upon the young scholar. Then the man's eyes wandered to the side and he gazed inquiringly upon the boy Asher.

"And who is this?" he asked. "Another Wilner?"

"No, rabbi," answered Asher. "I am the son of Menahem the scribe."

"Oh, yes, yes! You are the little son. Has your brother the bridegroom come back yet from Wilna?"

"He returned in the same coach with Elijah and your own son. I rode with them to your house."

"Ah!" the rabbi beamed. "It would be well for all our young people to go along with my boy, who is pious and learned. But you, little one, have done even better by accompanying Elijah. He is younger than you, but we judge people more by their learning than their years."

"I hope, rabbi," murmured Asher, "to have his learning too."

When Asher turned to go, Elijah again felt all forsaken. He held the bigger boy's arm, as though he feared to be left with these old people. And when they parted, the child buried his brimming eyes in his sleeve.

"The boy is homesick," said the *rebbetzin*.

"Study," said her husband, "is a cure for everything. Care for him and feed him, and then bring him to me."

As the woman and her charge entered the kitchen, the young rabbi came in to greet his father.

41

"Did you have a pleasant journey?" inquired the elder.

"Most of the way," was the answer.

"What do you mean by most? Did anything happen?"

"I think," spoke the son, "that Elijah will have to be watched carefully."

"Do not worry me with riddles!" expostulated the father. "Tell me exactly what you mean."

Rabbi Abraham thereupon recounted the episodes of the attempted robbery and possible kidnaping, while his father shook his beard in distress.

"Oh, my son!" he almost wept. "Only a month ago in Kobrin a boy who had just become Bar Mitzvah disappeared. The parents left ransom money under a tree in the forest, but the child was never returned. And in Chelm there were two cases; they stole the children of rich parents, who had to give all their possessions to get their sons back. Fortunately the boys were not harmed. But I fear the giving of ransom was a bad example. Now every thief and hoodlum in Poland will try to get quick returns by stealing Jewish children. But tell me—do you think anyone here knows about Elijah, about his learning and the wealth of his father?"

"It seems that there are some who do, father. The men who rode after us from Wilna will be sure to keep an eye on this house. Maybe they will wait a while because they want to allay suspicion, but I am afraid we shall have to watch the child every moment."

"A child like this," ruminated the elder rabbi, "is more precious than all wealth of gold and jewels. Israel will be saved not by money but by knowledge of the

42

Torah. I shall keep him at my side until a regular teacher
can be provided."

When Abraham entered the kitchen for his own meal,
he requested Elijah, who had already eaten, to return
to the study. This the boy did.

"Did you want me, rabbi?" he asked.

"Yes, my son. Sit here beside me."

A higher chair already stood by the rabbi's place,
and on this Elijah ensconced himself.

"Will you read in this talmudic tractate, my son?"

It was the treatise called Blessings, and the boy
rapidly read the text, translating into Yiddish with the
expressive singsong still employed by students of the
Talmud. Regularly he dipped into the commentary of
Rashi, printed at the side of the text, with such ease
and fluency as to astound the ancient savant.

"Never have I seen or heard a boy so young and
so capable," marveled the rabbi.

He closed the book and began making direct in-
quiries of the lad.

"When did you begin to study, little one?"

"I do not recall exactly," was the reply. "I always
studied."

"Even in the cradle?"

"One does not remember life in the cradle," said
Elijah, sagely.

"You are right," smiled the rabbi. "For a little boy
to know what one does not know is also a sign of intellect. You will do well, my son."

For a moment the boy closed his eyes. The long
journey was wearying, and for the first time he could
recall, he was disinclined to study. Still, one could not

be impolite to one's patron. He sat up and awaited further questioning.

Then he turned to glance out the window. Several children were running about lustily, and men and women were hurrying along the street. One of the bearded men looked very much like his father Solomon. He continued to gaze at the people without, while the rabbi fidgeted.

Into the mind of Rabbi David Katzenellenbogen there came a similar remembrance of times past. He too had been of tender years when he was sent off to become a scholar. And he had not been fortunate enough to be taken up by a town rabbi and his household. Instead, he had slept, with a dozen other youthful students, around the stove in the synagogue room of study, on pallets of straw. Each day he was provided with food by a different family near the academy and occasionally they supplied him with discarded garments and with a modicum of personal care. Unless the boys studied from morning to night, they grew fearfully homesick. Praying and learning were their only occupations. He had hardly known what it was to play.

Perhaps he should revise his notion that this boy too might forget his loved ones if he were kept perpetually at his books.

The rabbi turned again to Elijah, his voice suddenly tender and fatherly.

"Do you know, my son," he began, "that now you have came here to study you are really a man?"

"I shall be a man when I am thirteen," answered Elijah.

"I mean that you are a man in that now you will be self-reliant, now you will be able to get along just as though there were no one to watch over you. You are strong and brave."

"I am not strong and brave," returned the boy, soberly.

The rabbi looked up in surprise.

"I cannot fool myself," continued Elijah. "I miss my father and mother. I know they miss me. But it is my duty to become a scholar if I can; it is the duty of every Jewish child. And so I came here."

"I think," said the rabbi, "we will have no further learning today. Let me call my wife. She will take care of you."

The *rebbetzin* helped the lad unpack his belongings and put them away in a chest of drawers in a small room under the eaves. The bed was small, but well provided with linen. Then, having shown him the rest of the home he would occupy until the journey to Kaidan, she took his hand and led him into the street.

"You should see the city," she said. "Soon you will know everyone here, and they will help you pass the time happily."

"I was sent here for one purpose only," answered Elijah—"to study."

"Ach!" enjaculated the woman. "Some of our men were never children themselves. They know only study, study, all the time. From synagogue to study hall, and back to the synagogue—even food is not important to them. They would not even think of getting married if it were not for the matchmakers. Come, let us walk."

"Where are we going?"

"Nowhere. I'm a little afraid that the rabbi will want you to spend your first day here only over the books."

"He said I need not."

"And what did he suggest you do instead?"

"Nothing."

The *rebbetzin* raised her hands upward in a gesture of hopelessness. But even as she did so, the boy Asher came running across the cobblestones.

"Elijah, Elijah!" he called. "I've come back!"

The disconsolate seven year old waved his hand in greeting. A smile diffused itself over his still infantile features.

"I'm so glad, Asher!" he exclaimed.

The woman smiled also.

"All right, Elijah," she nodded. "You go ahead and play with Asher. I'll see to it that you boys have a little childhood. If the teachers keep you in too long, don't worry either. Wait till they fall asleep over their books, and then sneak out. But don't tell anyone I said so!"

The boys no longer heard her. They were running after the group first seen by Elijah from the window. And the little arrival from Wilna was having his earliest introduction to normal juvenile play.

4

LIFE IN BREST-LITOVSK

It is probable that his wife had spoken to the old rabbi, for in the morning, when Elijah awoke, there was no immediate call for him to enter the study. Instead, after a short prayer, the boy was given a breakfast of porridge and eggs and miraculously left to his own devices.

He went out and stood before the door of the rabbinical mansion. That is, this home might be so designated only in contrast to the great number of small frame houses in which the Jewish community resided. These were one-story buildings, whereas the rabbi and the wealthy citizenry dwelt in stone edifices all of two stories high, and often with an auxiliary room or two under sloping roofs.

From Elijah's station he could see the various residences of the important city and its important Jewish community. For the rabbi's house was at the apex of a street that sloped gently down in both directions. The boy could be seen at a distance clearly; and that is why he heard his name called by Asher far off.

Elijah, who still had not glimpsed the approaching youth, waved his hand in the general direction from which the sound had come. It seemed that Asher was walking in the shade of the houses and trees. He stepped out very suddenly before the astonished Elijah, who started and smiled in the same instant.

Asher was friendly and respectful.

"Good morning, Elijah," he said.

"Good morning," answered Elijah. "I am glad you came."

"Did you sleep all right?"

"Oh, yes, just as though I were at home."

"Is everything else all right?"

"They treat me very well."

"My brother and Esther say that you know more than the teachers in Wilna."

"I can't know more, because they taught me what I do know."

"You know as much then."

"No. The Talmud says that it is better to study a thing a hundred and one times than a hundred. They have had time to repeat everything many times; I have learnt each thing once."

Asher gazed in admiration at the younger lad.

"I believe you know more Talmud than I do. My father is coming from Wilna today; he always thought I was pretty bright, but when he talks to you—"

"I really haven't studied much," protested Elijah. "I came here to your city for that."

"That reminds me. Do you want to see the city?"

"Very much."

"Then, if the rabbi doesn't want you to study with him, I'll take you around."

Elijah, having obtained permission from the old pair who had become his guardians, was soon stepping through the narrow streets with his friend.

Asher pointed out the shops and stores owned by Jews.

"We have everything in Brest-Litovsk," he said, proudly. "You see, the Jews here have to supply what the army needs when it passes through."

"Then," commented Elijah, "they must make a lot of money from the government."

Asher shook his head.

"Oh, no! The government doesn't pay for army supplies. But we must give the soldiers meat and fish and oil and candies and paper and wax whenever they ask for them. It's like a tax."

Elijah looked concerned.

"Do you mean that the Jews have to give all the supplies to the army, and for nothing?"

"Sure. They only come once or twice a year. We have some big stores and warehouses here, so there is always enough."

"Do the gentiles have to support the army too?"

"No. That is for us alone. My father keeps the accounts, so I know all about it."

"But how," wondered Elijah, "do you get together all the money you need, to give to the *goyim*?"

"Lots of ways. We have taxes and licenses."

"Who collects the taxes?"

"The Jewish community, the *kahal*. They made my father the superintendent, and he gets money and presents of food for his work. When people sell salt or herring or tar or many other things, they pay him a tax. And every mill and tavern and brewery the Jews own must pay something. Besides, if a man wants to become a carpenter he must buy a license. The *kahal* collects on meat always, because only the community has the right to sell meat. Why, when a bride brings a dowry, they take off part as a tax."

"Then your brother's wife will have to pay too?"

"That's up to my father. Maybe Esther won't have to."

"Who pays the rabbi?"

"The *kahal*. Rabbis and judges and repairing the synagogue—everything comes from the taxes and licenses, and my father keeps the accounts."

"I hope," remarked Elijah, in apparent worriment, "you haven't any more expenses besides what you've told me about."

"Oh, I forgot something," said Asher. "Sometimes the messenger of the pope—they call him a *nuncio*—comes to visit, and then we have to give him and the church people presents."

Elijah refused to hear more. The idea of mulcting the Jewish community for so many purposes was a distasteful topic. He changed the subject of his queries to the life of the people about him. But this was the same as Jewish life in Wilna—trade, industry, travel, study, religious observance, and there was nothing new to be learned in the matter.

They traversed a large part of the town, and spent some idle moments on the bank of the Mukowetz. Returning by a different route, they visited the synagogue, the academy nearby, and other buildings employed for religious purposes. Then Elijah looked up toward the spire of the cathedral less than a quarter of a mile away.

"Let's look at the church," he suggested.

But Asher protested.

"It isn't always safe," he said. "Once I went by and some boys knocked me down because I didn't take my hat off when I passed. And sometimes when the people come out they buy papers attacking the Jews, and reading these makes them very angry and ready to hit the first Jew they meet."

"Are all the *goyim* like that?"

"Of course not. Most of them are all right to us, even the priests. My father says we can go to the courts just like any of them, and get debts or damages they owe us."

"Then all that's really bad here is the taxes."

"You're right."

Elijah now turned in admiration to the larger boy.

"You're terribly clever," he said, "to know all these things. I'm sure that lots of grownups in Brest-Litovsk wouldn't know as much about the city as you do."

"That's nothing," deprecated Asher. "I hear it all the time at home."

When the two boys returned to the rabbi's home, they were met by Abraham, the son.

"Did you see everything?" smiled the younger cleric.

"Yes, Asher took me everywhere except the cathedral," replied Elijah.

"You may see that soon, too," said Abraham, without further explanation. "My father wants to study with you before the noon meal."

Now that Elijah had obtained so much worldly knowledge, it was with some reluctance that he entered the study. But in a few moments he was so engrossed

in amassing learning that he wondered how he could
ever have imagined that anything else in the world might
approach it in importance.

Rabbi David Katzenellenbogen, for his part, was more
and more astounded by the brilliance of the lad. Elijah
asked questions of which ordained rabbis might be proud;
he answered other questions with surprising ease. Each
moment the rabbi peered down on him as to convince
himself that this youngster was in truth still but in his
eighth year.

At length both arose to eat the noonday meal, for
whtch the *rebbetzin* had been calling them for all of a
half hour. After the meal, the rabbi, instead of returning to his study, beckoned the boy to follow him toward
the academy.

"Today is court day," he said. "There will be three
judges; I am one. You have studied about the law—
now you are old enough and wise enough to see how
the law works. That is, you will hear how decisions are
rendered, sometimes on the basis of a generally known
law, sometimes on the basis of special laws laid down
by the community."

Elijah nodded happily. This too was to be an un-
expected adventure.

As the rabbi entered the academy hall the men and
boys present arose to honor him. Elijah was just behind
him; and at the behest of his guardian he too walked up
to the head table. At once the rabbi began to address
the assembly.

"Honored colleagues and students," he said, "it is
not customary to praise a man too fulsomely in his own
presence, but I wish to speak to you now not of a man,

but of a little boy. You have come here from all parts of Poland, Lithuania, and a large number of you have traveled from Germany and France to study and be ordained in our academy. We are all pleased with your achievements. However, the best prospective scholar in Brest-Litovsk is not any of you, but this lad at my side. He is Elijah, the son of Solomon Kramer of Wilna. At the tender age of seven he has been entrusted to our care here, and those who know him declare that he will prove the one in a generation or a century who will maintain the greatness of our people!"

There was a flurry about the large room, as the assemblage pressed to gaze upon the prodigy. Many had already heard rumors of a wonder child in Wilna. Here he stood before them, seemingly unconcerned by the adulatory address with which he had been presented, but looking about the room with the simple curiosity of the very young. In truth, he had hardly heard the words of the rabbi in his childish wonderment.

Then someone crashed his palm upon an open book and all became quiet. This was the signal that the court sessions were to begin. Elijah was given a chair near his mentor, while two additional rabbi-judges took their places on each side of Katzenellenbogen. As the proceedings were about to open, Elijah felt someone pressing toward him. It was Asher, who whispered excitedly into his friend's ear.

"You see the man who hit the book? That is my father. He is not only the superintendent of the taxes, and the scribe, but he is also the clerk of the court. He hears the complaints of the people, and then arranges for them to come here when the judges meet."

"And do you come here with your father always?"

"No, there are two reasons I am here. One is, my father and mother just came back from Wilna this morning. They were at Mordecai's wedding. So I want to be with him now. The other reason is that the first trial will be about Mordecai and Esther."

"About Mordecai and Esther?" queried Elijah, completely mystified. "Why, they just came to the city!"

"You'll see in a minute," answered Asher.

"What is the first case?" asked the rabbi.

At once Menahem the scribe arose to outline the matter at issue.

"We recently passed a rule that the dowries of brides can be taxed by the community. Now my son Mordecai came yesterday from Wilna, with his bride Esther, of that city. When I returned today, I found a note from the court asking that the tax be paid at once. Mordecai protested payment of any part of the dowry, because—"

"Please hold!" interrupted the rabbi. "You are only to tell us the case. Mordecai must plead for himself."

Upon this the bridegroom, with the full confidence of his eighteen years, stood before the judges' table.

"Honored, famed, and learned rabbis," he began, "as the first man to be involved in your new regulation about dowries, I arise to protest the demand made upon me and my wife. First, I believe no such impost should be laid, for every young couple starting in life has a right to the little given them to start with."

"That is not your province," spoke another judge. "The regulation has been passed. This is not the place to discuss repeal, but enforcement.."

"Then," said Mordecai, "I maintain that the law does

54

not apply to Esther. For everything her parents gave her was earned in another city, in Wilna. They paid taxes regularly to the community there. It is not right that goods or money should be taxed twice, merely because a bride wants to live in the same city as her husband."

Some of the students laughed at this unintentional sally.

"I would consent," continued Mordecai, "to pay for a local bride's dowry. After all, she has lived here all her life, and owes something to the community. But not Esther. Besides, suppose one of you had a daughter who married and left town. Would you want her to be taxed in the other city?"

"The argument seems muddled," remarked Rabbi Katzenellenbogen. "Do you think there is anything we can say to this young man offhand?"

There was a murmur of voices from the bench, and then a quick decision was rendered.

"Reb Mordecai the bridegroom," came the pronouncement, "it is not our function now to change community laws, but we believe the matter you present can be decided justly. Since Esther is a new resident, we cannot impose the full measure of the law upon her. But still she now lives in Brest-Litovsk, and has the status of a bride. Therefore we decide that she will pay half instead of all the tax regularly assessed."

Mordecai bowed in assent to this righteous judgment; and Menahem, his father, though still belligerent, thought better of protesting and proceeded hurriedly to the next case.

After three more minor cases had been presented,

Menahem electrified Elijah by announcing the next litigation to be between "Ezekiel Batlan and his wife Shprintze, of Wilna"! For the boy had known of these peculiar chracters and their quarrels, and had often passed their vegetable cart with his mother. Shprintze, without preliminaries, entered the fray.

"Rabbis!" she shouted. "I have pursued that good-for-nothing husband of mine all the way from Wilna. He took my hard earned money and climbed into the coach which was taking the wedding party back to this city. There was a coach leaving a few hours afterward, and when I found out he was gone, I came after him. For days we have been traveling, and only here did I catch up with him. Rabbis, he threatens to get a divorce, and I will not consent!"

"What is it you want of us?" asked a judge.

"I must tell you about this low creature. I have fed him and supported him for years. The best food on my cart I saved for him. And what have I asked in return? That sometimes he should watch the cart and make a sale. That he should not run off to gossip and mix into everybody's business every minute of the day. That he should be a man and not an insect!"

Here Rabbi Katzenellenbogen himself demanded that she be more explicit and less defamatory, and that she come to the point at once.

"I've told you, rabbis, what he wants," continued Shprintze. "He came here to run away from me, and to ask for a divorce in a strange place."

"And you still love him?" asked the rabbi.

"God forbid!" ejaculated the woman. "Who could love a worthless rascal like that? But every woman must

56

have a husband and a home. and I will not let that base scoundrel break up my home!"

There was laughter in the assembly, and a quick conference among the judges.

"Mrs. Shprintze," the decision was presented, "there seems to be no real case before us. No divorce has as yet been asked for. This is only a matter for reconciliation between husband and wife, and in the mean while this must be left to you and your husband."

"Reconciliation you want?" shrieked the embattled wife. "I'll reconcile him quick enough!"

She was indeed too quick for the cowering Ezekiel, whose exit was blocked by the press of students. In a trice Shprintze again held him by the ear, and her screaming denunciation could be heard through all the corridors as she dragged the husband who was so indispensable to some unknown battlefield.

The court broke up in unwonted hilarity. Elijah, as he departed in company with the judges, and trailed by a group of highly impressed young students, was smiling not because of his public laudation or the scene he had just witnessed. It was because Ezekiel Batlan and Shprintze, laughing stock though they were, represented to him some of the life of Wilna; and for the nonce he felt himself back in the beloved city of his birth.

5

THE NUNCIO

Asher had told Elijah of the occasional visits of the papal nuncio, the representative of the Vatican who traveled about inspecting all parts of Rome's religious empire. It was several weeks after the boy reached Brest-Litovsk that he was again reminded of this functionary.

For Rabbi Katzenellenbogen the elder, one morning after the regular divine service, declared that there would be no further study that day.

"There is an important conference of the rabbis and leaders of the community," he said. "You may come along if you wish."

Now Elijah had fallen into the idea held by most scholars of that era, that every moment spent away from Jewish study was a waste of precious time. He was seeing Asher more rarely, and he would not allow himself an hour of recreation. But if the rabbi thought a meeting was as important as study, then he would attend the meeting. Besides, the boy was conscious of the pride with which his mentor presented him to all companies in the city; and he enjoyed pleasing the rabbi. in that manner.

The group of ten gathered in a small room at the academy, Elijah sitting at the table as though he were a full-fledged member of the conference. The men seemed unusually earnest.

Rabbi Abraham Katzenellenbogen, the son, opened the discussion.

"My masters," he spoke, " at the best our stay in any of these central lands is a precarious one. We must support the army, pay excessive taxes, rule our own community, and remain at peace with the ruling religion. I am happy that my father, of Kaidan, who served in Brest-Litovsk in my place while I was gone to Wilna, and who is now staying on for a while before returning to his city, is here to advise us."

"What is the situation, son?" asked Rabbi David (as we may now call the father).

"We are faced," said Rabbi Abraham, "with the coming of the papal nuncio. Each time he has arrived in Brest-Litovsk we have given him a valuable gift, and also offered gifts to the officials of the cathedral. Many of our people say that we should cease making these offerings, that taxation is high enough already, and that we are fully protected as citizens in any case."

Rabbi David raised his hand to reply, not waiting for further details from his son.

"Let me tell you all," he expounded, "that even where Jews are apparently equal citizens before the law, the average gentile considers us as aliens and interlopers. He receives homage and presents from our people as though of right. Never assume that Jews will remain entirely secure in any land on earth, however liberal. Do you not remember the Golden Period in Spain, and what ultimately happened to us there? The story can be multiplied throughout history, in cities and nations everywhere. If you had never before given offerings to the nuncio or his associates, you might think twice before suggesting such an action. But once you have begun, it will be dangerous to cease. Do not, I beg of you, even consider the matter further."

None of the others spoke. They respected the visiting rabbi and father of their own spiritual leader too highly to oppose his views; but they knew too that his words were eminently wise. At length one householder rose to offer agreement with the views expressed.

"My masters," he said, "I do not think any of us will disagree with the words of the Rabbi of Kaidan. I know our own rabbi will not depart from the teachings of his father. If you will permit me, I shall make all arrangements to mollify the coming prelate with the appropriate gift."

It was so agreed, and the company broke up. The rabbis and little Elijah walked together.

"Little one," suddenly spoke Rabbi David, "I am getting old."

"Yes, rabbi," replied Elijah, dutifully.

"It is not easy for me to be a teacher."

"Yes, rabbi."

"Soon I shall leave Brest-Litovsk to return to my own city. Just as I took the opportunity of coming here to replace my son for a while, a young nephew of mine has been serving as rabbi in Kaidan. In a short while he is traveling north to his own new position, and I shall have to resume my old place. But there is another brilliant rabbi there who will better be able to teach you than myself. I shall only be able to supervise your instruction."

61

"Whatever you decide," exclaimed Elijah, "I shall not be among strangers."

"Very good," smiled the old rabbi. "In the mean while we shall continue studying together as before."

Despite Elijah's brave words he was not altogether at ease that night. He dreamt of his parents and of Wilna, and worried over the additional traveling he was to do. For he had made one set of friends in Brest-Litovsk, including Asher and other youngsters, and now he was to start forming entirely new relationships. He felt—as was indeed later the case—that his early life was to be a series of uprootings.

Neither were the two rabbis happy. The older man was to tear himself away from his beloved son again, and the young rabbi was once more to live apart from his parents. With the troubles attendant upon the coming of the nuncio, they could hardly feel any sense of ease.

During the next day the news was brought of the holy visitation from Rome. This was a Tuesday; the delegation would appear Thursday noon before the cathedral to receive the homage of the church and the populace. In the Jewish community preparations were being made. The regular gifts were prepared, and a large wagon decorated to carry them. Prominent householders had their best garments cleaned and pressed for the occasion.

On Thursday morning Elijah heard a fanfare of trumpets almost at his ears. He left the study to see what was going on, but Rabbi David hastily bade him return.

"It is the nuncio's party," he explained. "They pass

near our Jewish quarter. In the past Jews watching the procession have been accused of saying and doing disgraceful things, and there have been trials and executions as a consequence. All Jews living near the nuncio's route will shutter their homes and remain utterly silent until all have gone by. We shall have our hour later, at the cathedral."

But despite the shutters over the window of the study, Elijah could look out at the approaching cavalcade. A line of red-tunicked trumpeters rode first, on white horses. Behind them came a troop of cavalry. Then, in an open carriage, the papal nuncio rode alone, followed by his assistants in less pretentious vehicles. At the rear came a group of citizens, some of them bearing religious symbols on poles.

They waited until the sound of the trumpets had nearly died out before they ventured to reopen the shutters. Then, from various doors, came Jews of all sorts, to form a procession of their own.

There was a great hogshead on the cart leading the parade, with sundry smaller packages. The hogshead, filled with sugar, was the precious gift always offered the visiting dignitary by the *kahal* of Brest-Litovsk. Soon the company, led by the rabbis and communal leaders, all dressed in their best, drew up to the large square fronting the cathedral.

The doors of the cathedral were wide open. Before a huge assemblage of citizens the local curate and his clerk, in their churchly robes, offered an official welcome to the representative of Rome. He in turn, delivered a short address praising priest and flock for their loyalty to the Church, and hoping that soon all non-believers

63

would see the light and come into the great catholicity of the papal empire.

This reference to non-believers was evidently the signal for the Jews. Their procession advanced toward the cathedral steps, and then the householder who had made the arrangements stepped forward and bowed.

"Your Excellency," he said, "the Jews of this community, conscious of the friendship and protection of the great leader of the Catholic faith in Rome, desire to display their attachment to his representative, now gracing our fair city by his presence. The Jewish community herewith offers to you, as a very small measure of its esteem, the gift you see before you."

At once two brawny youths rolled the hogshead out of the wagon and set it up at the bottom of the stairs. Then they stood aside, while the speaker continued his presentations.

"We wish also," he announced, "to display our friendship for the curate who himself has been so friendly to us all. Permit me to offer you, Reverend Father, this bag of sugar. May the Lord sweeten the days of all of us!"

One of the youths took the pound of sugar—a most valuable commodity in those days— and handed it to the priest, with a deep bow.

"We have a gift as well," the speech continued, "for the clerk of the cathedral, to whom also we express our eternal amity."

Thereupon the other youth transmitted a flask of liquor to the clerk, whose eyes did indeed sparkle with pleasure. He knew that the Jews could not afford to offer

65

anything but the best drinkables to so exalted a parish personage as himself.

Now the nuncio turned to the Jewish assembly. All present, including little Elijah and his friend Asher, crowded up close.

"Ah, my friends." he began, "the great Father in Rome and myself will always weep for you, in that you have hardheadedly set yourself against the true faith. But we know well that in the days to come God will bring the truth home to you; and until then we shall look upon you as our brethren—poor benighted brethren, perhaps, but still all sons of our Master in Heaven. We accept your gifts with gladness, and bespeak for you the blessing of the Church and a happy future!"

Now, as expected, Rabbi Abraham approached to present his own compliments to the nuncio. That dignitary graciously offered the town rabbi his hand and wished him well.

"This is my father, Rabbi of Kaidan," added Abraham.

"I am happy to see you with us," was the greeting. "It always pleases us of the Church to meet men of learning and piety."

At this juncture the clerk whispered to the curate, who in turn addressed the nuncio in a low voice.

"Rabbi," spoke the latter, at length, "I am told that at this time there is in Brest-Litovsk a wonder child who is being trained in all the lore of the Hebrews. He is from the city of Wilna. It would please me to be able to talk to this child."

Rabbi Abraham, who knew what this kind of request portended, looked about in some misgiving for

66

the lad, who was near enough to approach directly he was summoned.

"This is the boy you have heard of," said the rabbi. Elijah, feeling that was expected of him, bowed his tiny frame in a somewhat frightened show of respect.

"You are a very handsome boy," said the nuncio; "the sort of boy Mother Church would be happy to possess."

"Thank you," replied Elijah. "I am glad you hear good things of me."

The dignitary bent as though speaking confidentialiy.

"Have you ever, my son, thought of studying the other religions besides your own, so that you may come to a proper conclusion at to which is nearest the truth?"

Rabbi David was shuddering lest the child give an argumentative answer, as might any loyal member of Israel. But he was reassured in a moment.

"I am very young," explained the sagacious child, "and have not yet had time to study everything I should like to know. At this time I am busy learning all that my Jewish masters can tell me; then, when I am a little older and can turn my attention to other studies, I shall surely want to know all that other teachers can impart to me."

"Well spoken!" smiled the nuncio, certain that his words has made a strong impression on the boy. "I shall hope some day to see you in Rome, where I may myself teach you some of the matters in which your present teachers may be deficient. You are a fine lad!"

Elijah bowed and hastened to stand behind the two rabbis, as though seeking for protection from the obvious wiles of one who would be happy to make him a *meshumad,* renegade to his religion. The reassuring pats of his rabbinical guides told him that he had spoken properly and in a manner to keep the dread official in good humor toward the Jewish community.

But the three were not yet permitted to depart. For the clerk and priest both came near to shake the lad's hand.

"The Church needs bright boys like you," openly declared the clerk. "We are hopeful that some day you will permit us to take you to Rome, to continue your studies under scholars of our faith."

The curate, however, was not so direct.

"My lad, we of the true Church know that one who studies the teachings of Catholicism must surely turn to us for salvation. Without doubt there will come the day, already spoken of, when one religion will be observed by all men on earth. Go in peace, my son!"

The churchmen now entered the cathedral, followed by many of the townspeople. The Jews turned and straggled back toward their own quarter, the empty wagon being driven rapidly past the pedestrians.

Rabbi David was tugging nervously at his grey beard, while Abraham was doing the same with his own black growth. Only Elijah seemed entirely at ease. Then Abraham called suddenly to the two strong youths who had served as giftbearers to the churchman.

"I should like to have you walk with us," he cried.

These and several others joined the group advancing over the broad expanse of paving plocks.

"Are you thinking as I am?" softly inquired Rabbi David.

"Most probably," replied the son. "When a nuncio

takes a fancy to a Jewish lad, that puts ideas into the minds of his followers. They say that there was at least one Jewish pope, and that he was stolen as a child and brought up as a priest. Not that the priests themselves would be so wicked, but there are misguided followers who are capable of anything in their blind devotion to their Church."

"Trouble, trouble, always trouble for the loyal Jew," sighed the elder.

"And what is more, even the converted Jew is often looked at with hostile eyes by those who most insisted on his being saved. The convert gains very little—except that in four generations his descendants may not be molested."

Thus conversing, the rabbis and their young charge were soon on more familiar ground. All about them were Jews and Jewish homes. As they reached the rabbinical mansion, Abraham again addressed his father on the matter of his stay in Brest-Litovsk.

"Father," he said, "I hope that you and mother will not hasten away to Kaidan. It is a rare occasion when I can have you with me so long."

"I must return to my community," sadly returned Rabbi David.

"And you will take the lad with you, too!"

"We are both attached to him, my son. But our duty is to his parents. He must be educated up to his capacity before he can go back to Wilna."

They spoke quietly, so that Elijah should not hear. For a few moments all three stood at the door, to bid farewell to members of the previous procession. The rest had departed, when suddenly Rabbi Abraham threw the door open, pushed Elijah within, and dragged his father along with him inside the house.

"What is all this?" demanded the old man.

"Oh. nothing," responded the young rabbi. "I thought for a moment that some of the church people were about, with their eyes on the boy. But I may have been mistaken. Forgive me for my violence!"

But Rabbi Abraham had not been mistaken. Lurking at the side of the house directly opposite he had caught sight of their old associates of the road, Stasz and Vanoff.

6

Kidnapers

Rabbi Abraham was somewhat dour during the day that followed. Ordinarily he would be happy and bustling on the day before the Sabbath. He spoke with sharpness to Elijah, when the boy suggested that he employ an hour roving through the town with his friends.

"There is little time!" he said. "You must spend all day studying if you are to become a scholar."

The rabbi's parents were as friendly as ever—even more so, for they seemed to be following Elijah whereever he went through the house.

But at noon Rabbi David, who had been instructing the lad, decided to make up for some lost sleep after his meal. Elijah again asked Abraham whether he might not spend some time in the open.

"There are wicked men abroad," replied the rabbi, "but I believe you will be safe if I go along. Come!"

Just before the door both stopped in surprise. For there, with a small cart piled with vegetables, stood Ezekiel Batlan and Shprintze, apparently reconciled after their public conflict of several days before. Ezekiel bowed deferentially.

"Ah, rabbi! and the young master!" he murmured.

Shprintze, hearing her spouse addressing others without her permission, turned irately, but subsided when she too looked at the pair. For a moment she was at a loss what to say to such distinguished personages, but her training came quickly to her aid. She bowed, then raised her voice in a raucous exhortation: "Cabbages, onions, potatoes!"

The rabbi and the boy laughed. In a moment of stress the woman could think of nothing to say but her ordinary sales call. But when they saw the woman's face flushing with embarrassment, they regretted their laughter. The rabbi decided to become a purchaser.

"How much are all these cabbages?" he asked.

"One zloty!" cried Ezekiel.

Shprintze was furious.

"Who is selling these vegetables?" she turned on her husband. "You or I? Who had the idea of borrowing the cart from Chaim Badjung? Who got the merchandise on credit? I or you? Be quiet or I will forget that I am a lady, a Jewess!"

"Now, Madam Jewess," said the rabbi, "you cannot sell your goods by quarreling in front of the customers. I'll buy the cabbages."

"What did I do?" demanded Ezekiel. "Did I hurt the sales? We need money to return to Wilna, so both of us can go back. Or perhaps, my wife, you want just enough to pay *your* way back?"

"What!" shrieked Shprintze. "Did I come here after you to return empty-handed? Such a year you should have! Get away from the cart! I'll do the business—oh, rabbi, come back, come back!"

Thus exhorted, Rabbi Abraham, aided by Elijah, carried into the house the purchase he had been on the verge of refusing in that embattled atmosphere. The two then returned to the street, to watch the happy pair as they screamed their way into the distance.

However, Asher soon arrived on the scene to suggest that they come with him to his school. The rabbi, for a reason he did not disclose, thought the idea one of the best he had ever heard.

He suggested that Elijah attend Asher's Talmud hour as an observer, while he examined some of the older students. Elijah, sitting on the fringe of the group surrounding Asher's teacher, was quite astonished to discover that he himself was fully acquainted with the text and subject matter under discussion. In turn the instructor, with his boys ten to twelve years old, looked rather fearsomely at the little visitor. So high was the reputation of the boy Elijah for precocious learning that the young teachers in the Hebrew school were troubled lest they make any minor error in his presence. But everything sounded correct to the lad, and he would have been too polite to suggest an amendment even if there had been an error.

In the meanwhile Rabbi Abraham was addressing a class of larger boys, preparing for ordination into the rabbinate.

"We have already discovered," he said, "that Elijah of Wilna promises to become the ornament of our age. His father is wealthy and he is highly honored by every community that knows him. Hence the boy is in danger. There are those who would take him and hold him for ransom, with peril to his life. And now other gentiles have heard how the nuncio and the officials of the Church would like to have the young genius in their own ranks. I fear that in the minds of ordinary criminals and of those who feel they will serve their faith thereby there is a strong desire to steal Elijah from us. He must be guarded. Who will help?'"

The students, almost a score of them, raised their arms in assent.

"But, rabbi," spoke one, "we have no weapons or horses. How shall we be able to fight them off?"

"Where can we find weapons?" immediately asked another student.

"Nowhere," sternly replied the rabbi. "All that some of our neighbors need is to find that young Jews are arming themselves—they would accuse us of designs on all Christendom."

"But what can we do then, rabbi?"

"Let there always be a group nearby, so that possible kidnapers may fear intervention or exposure. Such men do everything as secretly as possible."

Another rose to offer objection, just as though they were still engaged in talmudic argumentation.

"Suppose, rabbi, they come masked, and on horses. How will our presence help then?"

"You must do anything to protect the boy!" replied Abraham, with more vehemence than logic. "Fight them and their pistols; hold up the horses; but let no harm befall the child!"

When the rabbi's demands became purely emotional, there was no longer any purpose in pursuing the argument. The young men promised to serve as bodyguards —without unduly alarming little Elijah—and to suffer any assault rather than permit the wicked kidnapers to apprehend him.

One of the students must have talked too readily

outside the classroom, for in a few moments there appeared Menahem the scribe, his face elongated with worry.

"Rabbi, rabbi!" he cried. "They will take my son Asher!"

"Who will take your son Asher?" returned Abraham.

"The kidnapers! My boy plays with the boy from Wilna, and when they come they will steal him too!"

"They will take neither," firmly declared the rabbi. "We shall prevent it. But in any case they want only Elijah."

"But, rabbi, my son is precious too!"

"To yourself, Menahem, and to most of us, but not to prospective kidnapers. And please do not repeat what you have heard to anyone! You are likely to make more trouble than we can remedy."

The scribe seemed doubtful still. He was soon leading his protesting son out of his classroom and heading for his home. Evidently he believed no reassurances, even by the rabbi, where the safety of his child was concerned.

Rumor began rolling into a snowball at once. Women streamed into the school to fetch their little ones home. Small children were yanked in from the street. Men began carrying their walking sticks, poised like swords at shoulder level. Nothing that the now somewhat bewildered rabbi could do allayed their fears. He shrugged his shoulders and thought unpleasant thoughts about the talkative students and the gossiping Menahem.

Soon, however, the older students, who had closed their classes in expectation of the Sabbath, saw in the circumstance an opportunity to play at soldiers—a desire that seems to persist in all men, however pacifistic, most of their days. They were organized into squads to perform guard duty. With wooden sticks as muskets and swords they paraded in growing good humor all about the synagogue.

This too did not please the rabbi. The gentile population, despite the charges even then made against the Jew about his desire to conquer and rule the rest of humanity, looked upon their Israelitish neighbors as petty tradesmen, students, weaklings, slightly inferior testimonials to the greatness of their own religious teachings. It was not well for them to see boys drilling even in fun in the manner of the military. He summoned the youths once more into their classroom.

"Boys," he exhorted them, "do not make light of all I have told you today. You see how frightened are the parents of children in the city. More than once children have disappeared here and elsewhere; and what redress has any Jew in these times? Now, if you begin parading you will give wrong impressions to the gentiles. None of you are soldiers; you are just students whom I have asked to watch a threatened lad in secrecy. By all means make it secret, and not a jest!"

The young men were sobered.

"We shall be careful, rabbi," they promised. "We shall do what you ask of us, and no more."

Thus, when Elijah started on the short road homeward with Rabbi Abraham, a half dozen grown students strolled in the same direction, without ostentation. The sharp-eyed boy noted their coming, however.

"Rabbi," he asked, " did you invite some of the students for the Sabbath?"

"They are probably just promenading," evaded the rabbi. "There is no class this afternoon, and they are taking the air."

"But other times they walk close together, and now they keep their distances, singly and on both sides of the street."

"You see too many things, boy," laughed the rabbi, somewhat uneasily. "It just happens they are busy with their own thoughts. They all come from other cities, and must be thinking of their loved ones. You too sometimes speak of your parents during the long Sabbath."

Elijah did not answer. And Rabbi Abraham at once regretted bringing back to the boy remembrance of his early homesickness.

When they reached the rabbinical home, the students also stopped, pretending to be interested in their surroundings. Thus the entire group formed a momentary tableau, until there came the sound of quarreling from the other direction.

Here were Ezekiel Batlan and Shprintze again, once more—or perhaps still—engaging in domestic pleasantries. The students ran happily to surround the pair and their cart. Most of the stock had been sold—and this seemed to be the cause of the present dissension, which was carried on without regard to the quickly convened audience.

"I knew I should not trust you," Shprintze was assailing her cringing spouse. "I go away for a minute, and there are no vegetables left, practically, when I return. You could not have eaten them raw—you with your delicate stomach which I am always pampering. Then we count up the money. I should have twice as much. Where are you hiding it? As certain as I was Shprintze Bebelfresser before I was fool enough to accept your proposal of marriage—"

"I didn't propose!" interrupted Ezekiel, weakly.

"What? I'll crack your ears for you! You pursued me everywhere. When I went to visit your mother, who was there also? You. When I happened to be in your father's store, who was always leering at me from behind the counter? Only you. Everywhere, in the street, in the synagogue, at joyous occasions, wherever I was, there were you also!... But don't let me get away from the subject, ruffian!... Give me that money! Give it to me, or so help me heaven, I shall throw you in the dust and in the presence of all the world take it out of your pockets or wherever you have concealed it!"

What happened at this moment was too sudden and confused to be noted in completeness by any one person, but the several accounts dovetailed into this pattern.

With the tremendous female voice filling the air, none of the principals or volunteer bodyguards were able to hear the approach of two men on horseback. These persons dismounted in the space between two houses and crept up casually on the rabbi and his charge. Before anyone became aware of what was happening, one sent the rabbi sprawling over his own threshold and the other snatched the boy under his arm. Then both started wildly for their horses.

But at the same time Shprintze, violently aroused, had raised her hand to strike down the object of her affection and her hate. Ezekiel, trying to escape, pushed the cart immediately in to the path of the two malefactors. The haste of the kidnapers sent the cart and

its contents into the roadway, throwing them too into the dust beyond. Elijah was dropped before the men sprawled over the pavement, and he remained unharmed.

While the fighting pair were too dumbfounded to continue their debate, the students, quickly aroused, rushed to pick up stones and sticks to hurl after the retreating and discomfited assailants. The men reached their horses, mounted and spurred them on, but not before one of them had felt a wooden block carom off his head. The man's cap fell into the dust.

Rabbi Katzenellenbogen quickly recovered, and rushed to the aid of Elijah, who arose altogether unhurt and hardly conscious of the quick procession of events in which he had been involved. The rabbi saw the cap on the ground and recognized it as the kind worn by the unremitting villains Stasz and Vanoff. The students surrounded them both, happy that there had been no casualties.

Ezekiel and Shprintze were still speechless. They gazed mournfully at the foodstuffs lying begrimed about them. But the rabbi hastened from Elijah's side to comfort them.

"My friends," he said, "you have without intention saved this boy from death or worse. We can see that God will use even the peculiarities or sins of men for a good purpose. You came to this city from Wilna by accident. It was the will of Heaven that you should quarrel at this moment, and save the crown of Israel's youth." He smiled at the assembled students. "Now, see how much you can save of your wares. I shall buy them all!"

Rapidly the quickly reconciled pair gathered up the

grimy vegetables and carried them into Rabbi Abraham's house. He too entered, returning with a purse, from which he dispensed a generous sum to the ill-married couple. They looked at the money and suddenly fell into each other's arms with whoops of joy.

"Now we can return to Wilna!" cried Shprintze. "Come, my darling Ezekiel! My lovely partner, everything will be well with us!"

But Ezekiel was coy.

"Will you promise not to hit me again?" he demanded.

"I promise, I promise! Come, let us see if there is a carriage going off today."

"I am sorry," spoke the rabbi, "to remind you that the Sabbath will soon be here, and you cannot start your journey today. But"—as he saw the crestfallen looks in both faces—"I shall find a place for you both until Sunday, where you can lodge and eat."

Shprintze and Ezekiel Batlan bowed their thanks, their features beaming with the happiness of newly-weds.

Then the rabbi's face grew stern again.

"I want to thank you boys," he addressed the students, "for having tried to help me keep Elijah secure among us. I had no thought, when I spoke to you this morning, that the emergency would arise so soon. Please come here in the morning, so that we may all go to synagogue together. Until then I shall keep Elijah in the house."

The child, who had felt no fright until after the adventure, scurried through the door. Abraham followed to seek his father, who had evidently heard nothing of the recent commotion.

"Father," he said, "it is my sorrowful request that you and mother leave Brest-Litovsk for your own home immediately after the Sabbath."

"Why, what has happened, my son?"

"There is danger here for young Elijah. Only a few minutes ago the evil ones attempted to abduct him, and God interposed to foil their plot."

Rabbi David knit his brows.

"Then we must go. Perhaps I was in error in staying with you so long. In Kaidan the lad will have the right teacher. Do not worry further, my son. All will be well with Elijah."

When Elijah slept over the Sabbath eve he had a presentiment of angels standing about his bedside. But they were no angels who in groups of four remained on guard all night thereafter about the home of Rabbi Katzenellenbogen. These were the advanced students of the academy, who had constituted themselves the determined bodyguard of Wilna's famous child.

7

LIFE IN KAIDAN

There was great excitement in the community of Brest-Litovsk on the Sabbath following the assault on Elijah of Wilna. In the synagogue groups gathered before and during the service to discuss the peculiar circumstances of the boy's deliverance. Ezekiel was called to the desk and honored with a portion from the Pentateuchal reading. Elijah himself, flanked even in the sacred edifice by his student bodyguard, had to repeat the special blessing recited after a long journey or a rescue from danger.

Rabbi David, who was to depart with the boy on the morrow, delivered a short address after the Bible reading. He lauded the community, once more commended his son to them, and praised the grace of God that had spared Elijah to the coming generation.

There were sighs from the women's gallery when Elijah's departure was mentioned. The handsome lad with the grave eyes had impressed himself on many a motherly heart. The boys who had seen Elijah at the school or academy felt that he was taking with him a newly established glory of their city. It was almost like the leave from Wilna—hope and pride and sadness inextricably welded.

The carriage for the journey was to be specially hired for the purpose. Only the old people and Elijah

83

were to ride within. On the driver's seat there were to be two armed trustworthy drivers; and behind the coach an armed horseman to serve as additional protection. A fortune in precious jewels could not have been better guarded.

A hundred townspeople asembled at the young rabbi's house to witness the departure. Men and women, with a number of small children, crowded the space about the carriage. While the rabbi and his parents were making their farewells, Elijah peered through the crowd in evident search of someone. His search was unrewarded, for he still gazed about through the window when all were already embarked.

But as the horses started off, three newcomers shouted wildly to the driver to stop. These were little Asher, his brother Mordecai, and the bride Esther. They were heard, and the driver reined in, somewhat angrily.

"What's wrong?" he asked.

"It's Asher! I'm late! I want to say goodby to Elijah!"

Elijah bounded from the halted equipage and shook the hands of all three. Esther bent down and kissed him.

"Goodby, little scholar," she said. "May all your journeys everywhere be happy ones!"

The last glimpse of Asher, his playmate and admirer, brought tears to the eyes of the young traveler. If only partings were not such wrenches of the heart, he thought, his pursuit of learning in alien places would be a pleasing adventure.

Adventure? he pondered again. He was living through many strange and perilous incidents, all endured for the greater glory of his faith. Study was equivalent to all other virtues, for knowledge made men free, just, helpful, and righteous.

At midday they stopped at a pleasant inn, which had the added merit of being overshadowed by great overhanging shade trees. There was a well directly in front of it; from this all travelers might drink freely.

None of the journeyers wanted to haste away from so pleasant a spot. The driver, sipping the kind of drink that is seldom cool, called a conference of guardians to establish rules for their further protection, should danger threaten. It was decided that whenever they encountered suspicious groups, particularly such as rode on horses, they should draw and extend their weapons at once. Thus, if the others were peaceable men, no harm would be done; if not, they would be in an immediate position of defense.

Whether these precautions were necessary they could not know. In any case, none of the riders met with on the road made any effort to molest them. Occasional very light rains settled the dust sufficiently to render their progress mildly pleasurable. There were more trees, better hostelries, and a number of small streams with wooden bridges. Animals of the field frequently crossed their path, and once the driver pulled up the horses just as they were about to run down a quite lazy and inquisitive cow.

The arrival in Kaidan proved a general celebration. How the populace had learned of the coming of their rabbi no one could ascertain. No letter could have passed that way ahead of the carriage; and there were no other forms of communication in those times. In all likelihood some person on the outskirts of the city had glimpsed the returning cleric, and had hastened to spread the information throughout the neighborhood. When they approached the Katzenellenbogen home at the slow rate compelled by the narrow, crowded streets and the jolting cobblestones, the travelers found a large welcoming committee facing them. The gathering was led by a group of graybeards, the elders of the community. With these stood two younger men, blackbearded.

"Welcome back to your city!" cried the leading dignitary.

The rabbi was surrounded by happy, shouting householders, all reaching for his hand. The *rebbetzin* too held court at a side. While the trio who had conveyed them thither wiped their sweaty brows, Elijah stood aloof, again a lonesome and heartsick boy.

Than the rabbi pointed him out to his people, and in a trice Elijah found himself encircled by all the men and women in the party. His eyes were teary as grown men, some in the eighties, pressed to shake his tiny hand. Their smiles and greetings, however, encouraged him greatly. He began to feel safe and beloved in this strange place.

The rabbi then presented his nephew Kalman, who had temporarily held the rabbinate in Kaidan while the old man visited his son in Brest-Litovsk. Rabbi Kalman patted the child's head, and then engaged the driver in conversation.

"We shall return toward Brest and then go your way," promised the coachman. "If you can get a party together, we'll be able to take you."

Upon this Kalman hasted busily among the householders to learn whether any present wished to join him on his journey. For now that his uncle had returned he could go on to the clerical post which had already been offered him.

The other young rabbi who greeted Elijah did not leave his side, however. This was Moses Margalit or Margolis, thorough scholar and teacher, whose ability had been heralded in all the Polish and Lithuanian communities.

"Rabbi Moses will be your instructor," announced Rabbi David.

The happy smile with which Moses took the boy's hand and patted his cheek at once endeared him to the lonely Elijah. The little one felt a sudden desire to return to his studies and make his parents proud of his achievements in Talmud and the Law.

With some difficulty the guards pressed through the crowd to carry the baggage into the house, another pretentious two story structure provided for the town rabbi. A number of the welcoming group followed after, and these were supplied with liquor and cakes by the housekeeper. The old servant grumbled a bit, but her eyes lit up when the looked upon the lad who had come to join their household.

"A fine, handsome boy you are," she said, her wrinkled face beaming. "You will be a great scholar and a great man in Israel. While you are away from your parents you need not worry. I shall take care of you as though you were my own."

The housekeeper, called Chaya, led the boy to the rear of the house, where she doused his hands and face from a basin of cool water. Then she dried off the water, patted down his hair, brushed off his clothes with a broom-like contrivance, and conducted him to a large diningroom, where sat the rabbis and half a dozen visitors. Kalman arose as Elijah entered.

"You will sit and eat with us," he said. "This is my final meal here and your first. You should be honored by leading the grace after meals, but you are still a minor under the law, so the honor is mine. But you will say the grace over bread."

Rabbi David nodded assent to Elijah. The boy, followed by his elders, washed his hands at a large brass water container on the wall, turning a tiny faucet to obtain a trickle of fluid. Then he recited the blessing for bread in a loud voice, and sat down to eat with the others. Everyone wore a glistening silk skullcap provided by the *rebbetzin*.

That worthy woman herself brought in the entree, the fish, the soup, the roast, and the stewed fruit comprising the homecoming banquet. Chaya had the prosaic task of clearing the dishes. Her glance always turned to the little lad in that adult assemblage, whom she determined to mother as she had done her own brood, long ago grown, married, and dispersed.

The lay head of the congregation, having eaten his roast, arose to utter a few words and properly improve the occasion.

"Rabbis, gentlemen!" he proclaimed, "we have with us the already famed Wilna genius, who has been brought here to study under Rabbi Margolis by our own honored rabbi. The Talmud tells us to honor our students, because they may some day become greater than ourselves. In the case of young Elijah of Wilna we already know his greatness, and I welcome him to Kaidan in the name of the entire Jewish community."

Elijah, somewhat bewildered, looked up with wide eyes. Perhaps it was the custom here to greet guests, large or small, with such fair phrases. At any rate, the attention they were according him was not unpleasant. He was going to like his stay in Kaidan.

The rabbi, however, frowned a bit, from the head of the table. He was wise enough to understand that this kind of adulation was not advisable for any little boy. He at once turned to his dessert, in which all the guests followed him, and called upon his nephew to lead the grace.

The visitors departed singly, until only the congregational head remained with his spiritual leader. Elijah laid his head on the arm of a leather chair near the window and soon was half asleep. The journey, the heavy meal, and perhaps the heavy air, had made him drowsy.

Thus he heard the strange conversation that followed.

"Perhaps, rabbi," spoke the synagogue president, "you were angry that I publicly praised your young genius?"

"A little," admitted the rabbi. "He is not yet eight years old, and a student, as well as a grown scholar, must be taught to be humble."

"Well, I am sorry, rabbi, but I had a purpose."

"A purpose?"

"Yes. Now my son Chatzkel is a man of piety and learning, and besides he has a fine business in hides and leather. He has a beautiful big home, with much room, and—"

But the rabbi, understanding the man's purpose, interrupted him.

"You are kind," he said, "but I must have the boy here where I can supervise his education. And if you fear that the expense of keeping him may be beyond my means, do not worry. His father has wealth, and he will be glad to send money for the child's support whenever necessary."

"Well, you see," rejoined the other, "I was thinking not alone of that, but of the necessity of providing so brilliant a student with a suitable wife. Oh, not now— he is several years too young yet—but when the time comes. My son, you know, comes of a very good family —of my family, of course—and it would be an excellent idea to join a child of his with the family of Wilna. Chatzkel has a daughter of six—a beautiful child, already reciting the blessings, learning how to be a good Jewess, bright beyond her years—and I am certain that we can form a preliminary arrangement between the two little ones."

The rabbi was thoroughly embarrassed.

"Your words are sensible, Reb Beinish," he said. "But after all, I am not the child's father, and have no right to arrange his marriage."

"Then," spoke the man, in the tones of one who never fails to carry out any of his expressed purposes, "I shall set off at once for Wilna to speak to the parents."

The rabbi's hand was raised in mild objection.

"That will not be necessary, Reb Beinish. The parents will undoubtedly came soon to visit their son, and I am certain that then you will be able to broach the subject readily."

"That is better," agreed Reb Beinish. "I have no doubt that the parents will be happy to join my family and assure their son of a happy life in the days to come, with leisure to study and become a leader of his people. The matter is practically concluded."

When the visitor had gone, the rabbi shrugged his shoulders, smiled, and proceeded toward the kitchen, to relate the incident to his wife. Elijah, resting comfortably in the shadow of the armchair, thought the talk about his marrying a very good joke, and gave it no further consideration. Why, a boy should be at least thirteen, a Bar Mitzvah, before he became engaged! It would take him at least until that time to learn everything his Jewish instructors could teach him, with the other secular and general subjects that might be permitted him.

Chaya came in search of the boy. She made him follow, and soon he entered the room in which his early student years were to be spent. He found it much larger than the chamber he had occupied in Brest-Litovsk, and the bed was large enough for two people. The feather-bed on it was covered by a spread of intricate pattern that must have taken a year's leisure from the life of some industrious Jewish housewife. The window was large, and looked out on a clump of small trees and a profusion of wildflowers. Everything was so neat and pleasant that the boy clapped his hands in joy.

Chaya was pleased at Elijah's gesture. She arranged his articles of wear in sundry drawers, and gave him complete instruction in the ways of the household. All this the boy hearkened to with grave earnestness.

Sitting at the window, looking out at the beauties of nature without, Elijah sleepily allowed the remem-

brances, happy or unpleasing, of the past weeks, to range
themselves in his mind. Father and mother seemed very
far away, and all the associations of his infant years.
He saw Brest-Litovsk again, Asher, the highwaymen, the
young rabbi, the newlyweds, the pistols in the belts of the
guards, the books he had studied—every detail of these
crowded days now gone from his life.

He might have fallen completely asleep during these
musings, except that every few minutes, it seemed, the
voice of the rabbi was raised in discussion with some
guest. Undoubtedly the home of the rabbi, being open
to all, must be the scene of many argumentations and
takings of counsel.

At length the boy descended the stairs and looked
through the doorway at the buildings and people he was
to live among. As he stood there a man came out of the
rabbi's study, apparently crestfallen, and brushed hard
against him. The man turned.

"Are you Elijah of Wilna?" he asked.

"Yes, sir. I have just come."

"A fine boy, a fine boy!" murmured the departing
visitor. "It is too bad, too bad nothing will come of it!"

A moment later another visitor entered and stopped
to look at the boy.

"Are you Elijah of Wilna?" he too inquired.

"I am, sir," returned the perplexed child. "I came
here today with the rabbi, from Brest-Litovsk."

"Ah," was the comment, "that is very good. You
are a fine boy. Something good will come of this."

The voices that Elijah now heard from the rabbi's
study were loud and violent. He was alarmed lest the
newcomer had come to do injury to his friend and patron.

92

But even as he feared for Rabbi David, the door of the study was thrown open and the rabbi appeared with his hand firmly grasping the shoulder of the visitor, whom he was propelling with ministerial gentleness to the door.

"You will please say nothing more and go away!" exclaimed the angry cleric. "No, I will not hear a word. The boy is seven years, he has just come here to spend years in study, and already you are the sixth matchmaker who has come to get him engaged or married. I am a man of peace, but I tell you if another *shadchan* dares to broach that subject again to me today, I shall throw him bodily out of the house!"

The interloper started to run down the street as though he actually feared violence at the hands of the pacific spiritual leader. But Elijah thought the scene very funny. As he slipped his hand confidently into that of Rabbi David, both laughed until Chaya and the *rebbetzin* rushed in in alarm to quell the commotion.

8

THE STUDENT

We have traversed some weeks in the life of Elijah; now we may pass through the years. For there began in Kaidan a course of instruction that took all the boy's time, and was designed to provide a grasp of every important source of Jewish teaching. Sabbath afternoons were also devoted to Bible instruction, although Elijah had long passed the period of groping in the Scriptures and their commentaries. On festival days he sometimes joined the less gifted lads from the Hebrew school in play. This was rare, however; the brilliant student was forgetting how to gambol after the normal juvenile manner.

For two years his preceptor plied Elijah with advanced Bible interpretation; with study of the Halakah, the legal portions of the Talmud and later codes; and of Aggadah, the legendry, wisdom, and incidental discussions of the talmudic literature. At nine he was so far advanced in these normal subjects of study, that the rabbis looked about for something difficult enough to hold his interest. And at that tender age Elijah was initiated into the mysteries of the Kabbalah.

Now the Kabbalah comprises the mystic writings, filled with hidden meanings, which describe the relationship between God and men. Much of it is almost impossible of explanation, and often it is a mere conglomera-

95

tion of words. There are descriptions of the various spheres through which one ascends from earth to heaven. There are new interpretations of simple sentences in the Bible. The language of the Zohar and other holy writings of the Kabbalists is extremely difficult. All this was given to the nine-year-old to read and study.

The child was not greatly impressed. He was a very sensible, hardheaded little person who, while a strong believer in God's Law, could not stomach the strange pictures of God and the world which these writers of religious puzzles presented to him. He wanted to see the world not alone as a religious creation, but also as a living, material substance on which one could firmly plant one's feet.

When the people of Kaidan, and even Moses Margolis, his chief teacher, were proclaiming that Elijah already knew everything, they meant that he was acquainted with all the truths enclosed within the many large yellow leather tomes of Jewish lore in the rabbi's study and the academy. It was Elijah himself who brought up the subject of additional woredly study.

"Rabbi Moses," he said, "I want to learn what men have found out about nature and the heavens above the earth."

The rabbi looked puzzled.

"Do you not know," he asked, "that all things important in heaven and earth are to be discovered in our Holy Writings and our Talmud?"

"I am certain," replied Elijah, "that these tell us correctly how to live, how to love God, how to do His commands—but not enough about the actual conditions under which we live on earth."

"You may be right," said Moses, "I too have dab-
bled a little in science and in languages, and in other
matters not covered—not completely covered—by the
Torah and Talmud. But there is a danger that you will
turn away from Jewish studies altogether if you become
too engrossed in these other matters."

Elijah shook his head.

"I shall continue everything I have been learning with
you," he promised. "I shall even go on with the Kabbalah
until I understand it fully, no matter how long that may
take. But I still want books on anatomy and astronomy
and other sciences. What I have read about them in the
Talmud has only increased my appetite."

"You are a pious lad," admitted Moses, "and I am
not afraid that your head will ever be turned away from
your own people and religion. I have some of the books
you need in my home, and I shall bring them tomorrow."

His first secular volume was one about the stars.
Each day, after he had completed his full assignment
of Hebrew study, the boy pored over the book, noted
the charts and the positions of the then known stars
and planets, and went out into the night to learn what
he could from the heavens themselves. His rapid mind
soon committed to memory all that he saw, so that he
was able thereafter to read the skies like one of his talmudic treatises. He had no telescope, unfortunately,
hence could not make some of the many additional dis-
coveries that are now the glory of modern astronomy.

Then Rabbi Moses gave the boy a magnificent large
work on botany, with colored pictures of the plants of
the field. It became necessary for him to study nature

at first hand, just as he had turned from the pictures
of the stars to the stars themselves.

It was through this desire that he began, for the
first time since his life in Wilna, to take walks into the
country. He looked on the waysides for herbs and flow-
ers and strange growths not recorded in his book. And
then he determined to seek further information from
the tillers of the soil themselves.

One late afternoon Elijah reached a farm a half
hour's walk from his home. He approached the farm-
house and knocked on the door. The house was a large
barn-like structure, with a single door and two openings
at the side, in lieu of windows.

The door opened, and a heavily-built, coarse peasant
emerged, followed by a slatternly female and a brood of
dirty, half-naked children. As though these were insufficient, several ducks and chickens came after them,
then one pig and two dogs. Elijah saw the outline of
a horse in the rear of the large room, feeding at a
trough.

"What do you want?" surlily demanded the farmer.

"I want to learn about plants," timidly replied the
boy.

"Then why do you come to us?" responded the
peasant.

"You see—it is because—you work in the fields
and can tell me about nature."

The entire family joined in laughter.

"Be off, you!" was the command. "Learn about
plants yourself. We are busy enough feeding ourselves
and our livestock!"

Elijah attempted to enlist the aid of other tillers

of the soil, with like results. He was driven off the land, once cursed for being a Jew, and in general made sport of. The lives led by the peasants revolted him. All seemed to live in filth, humans and animals together. He lost all heart for a study which should have come to him from the soil, but had to be learnt in books alone. Having read what he could find on the subject, he turned away from the study of botany.

Yet all that Elijah read he remembered. In the years to come he was to recall every fact in the large volume Rabbi Moses had lent him, even as he never forgot a lesson in the Talmud.

Thereafter the lad developed a huge interest in mathematics. Frequently the Talmud and its commentaries presented lengthy discussions of distances and dimensions. Elijiah thought it would be an excellent thing for himself and other students to know all that could be learnt about such subjects before attempting this kind of reckoning.

When Moses first permitted him to peer into a Euclid or geometry, Elijah's first thought was that this book ought to be translated into Hebrew. Moses was appalled.

"Can you think of no better work for a Jewish scholar than to render all these non-Jewish subjects into the sacred tongue?"

"But there is nothing non-Jewish in this," objected Elijah. "They do not treat of idol worship or strange religion. There are subjects that belong to all men."

"Well, perhaps you are right about mathematics," assented Moses. "But we cannot allow these things to go too far. After all, our Jewish boys must pay most attention to their Jewish studies."

"Have I neglected any?"

"No. In your case I see no harm."

"Then give me instruction in mathematics!"

"You ask me too much," Moses shook his head. "I have only looked at the Euclid, and I am not able to explain it."

"Then who is here who can teach me?"

The rabbi showed confusion in his features, but somewhat haltingly made reply.

"There has just come to the church here a new priest, who is reputed to be very proficient in the science of numbers."

"Then I shall go to him!" declared Elijah.

"What are you saying?" cried Moses. "How can you, a young lad, go to a church to study?"

"He will not convert me," said Elijah, resolutely.

Rabbi Moses, perplexed, decided to discuss the matter with the old rabbi, who also protested the idea as near blasphemy. The discussion raged for several days, until a compromise was arranged with the ambitious boy. The teacher was to accompany Elijah to the priest, and stay there only long enough to obtain guidance for the child's further study.

The rector of the local church lived in a small brick home near his place of worship. It was with hesitancy that the pair struck the huge knocker on the door, and waited to be admitted.

It was the priest in his regular frock that opened the door to them. He looked from one to the other, then suddenly smiled.

100

"I remember you, boy!" he cried. "You should remember me, too. I am Father Zema, who less than three years ago talked to you in front of the cathedral —when the nuncio honored us with a visit."

"Then we are both of Wilna!" returned Elijah.

"Yes. Will you come into my sitting room?"

Once seated within, Rabbi Moses announced his name and business.

"Ah!" spoke the father. "Is it possible that your young charge has remembered what we said to him in Wilna and is desirous also of learning something of our own teachings?"

Here Elijah made a surprising statement.

"Father Zema! I have already studied in my books what Catholics believe, but I still remain true to my own faith. Cannot you forget your aim to convert us all for a little while? They say you are very learned in mathematics, and have taught it also. Now I come to you to learn only this subject—this and nothing more."

The priest smiled. In any case he could form a closer friendstip with the brilliant youngster, and he was flattered that one should come to him for instruction in a subject unrelated to the church. He took a book from the shelf without further parley, and opened it to Elijah's gaze.

"Now this," he said, "is an easy way of learning. If you cannot understand any of the Polish words I shall be glad to go over the pages with you and explain them as well as the propositions."

"Please begin at once, Father Zema," said Elijah.

Thus did the priest assist the boy in attaining the

fundamentals of scientific training. The rapidity with which Elijah learnt was amazing to the father, who often regretted that he could not mingle discussions of church doctrine with his mathematical formulas. Always Rabbi Moses was present, however. In any case, there had been an agreement to stick to the subjest, which a good churchman was not permitted to violate.

Gradually Father Zema began to respect the child as his superior in mentality. On occasion he asked advice on troublous matters of the parish, which Elijah, employing the principles and modes of thinking in the Talmud, settled with the wisdom of a Solomon.

The community was at length treated to the strange phenomenon of the parish priest paying an unannounced visit to the home of the local rabbi. The astounded maidservant asked if he wished to see the rabbi.

"No," replied the curate. "I have come to ask an audience with the boy, Elijah of Wilna!"

There was a scurrying about to provide the best chair for the unusual guest and then to call in the lad thus honored.

Elijah shook the proffered hand and also sat down.

"I should like to talk to you in private," said the priest, "but not on religion!" he hastened to add, as the two rabbis frowned slightly and made a protective gesture toward the lad.

They were seated near the window, both mathematicians, when the priest began.

"Elijah," he spoke, "you are a wise child, wise beyond your years. You can help me in a very important matter."

"I help you?" queried the wide-eyed lad.

"Most certainly. I want you to imagine yourself a curate in a Catholic parish."

Elijah waved his hands uncertainly.

"No, no!" laughed Father Zema. "I am not trying to convert you. But I seek advancement in my church, and I am writing a letter to Rome about my ambitions. Several laymen have already approached the pope, and I believe the nuncio you remember is friendly toward me. What I want you to do is tell me what you think you would say if you were in my place."

"If you think I can help you," began Elijah.

"You can! I know what the Talmud does to sharpen the minds of Jewish students."

The extraordinary request was quickly fulfilled. For Elijah said that he would first tell Rome of his career and achievements, and then ascribe any success of his to the inspired leadership of the head of the Church. Then he would prepare figures of the growth of this parish, and express hope of ever greater growth. Finally, he would remind the papal office that for long no bishop had served in that section of the country, and that for the sake of the Church he hoped that an appointment might be made at an early time. That is, he would say all these things if he were himself Father Zema—and he would say them in a simple, brief, and devoted manner.

"Magnificent!" cried the curate, quickly thanking the lad and hastening to pen his letter.

When the boy was alone, he was visited by a greatly concerned pair of rabbis.

"What does he want of you?" cried Rabbi David, in evident anguish of spirit.

"Nothing," replied Elijah. "He promised not to try to convert me, and all he asked now was advice concerning a letter."

"Still," broke in Rabbi Moses, "I am afraid that this business of studying strange subjects and going to churchmen for assistance will do you harm. They will pursue you, and perhaps steal you away from us."

"I was almost stolen once,'" said Elijah, "but not by the Church. It would be no use to them now, because they could never convince me, even under torture."

"Still I am worried," said Rabbi David, "though we know how pious and trustworthy you are. You must promise us no longer to go to this priest for instruction. If you want to learn new subjects we shall send away even to Warsaw to get Jewish instructors for you."

"I can promise that," declared Elijah. "You are in place of my parents and can forbid me anything. It was only for a little while that I went to Father Zema, and he only told me how and what to study in his book."

"A bad business," the old rabbi still shook his head and looked reprovingly at Rabbi Moses, who commented merely, "Do not fear. He is safe from the Church."

Thereafter Elijah remained with his Jewish teachers and no longer sought non-Jewish help in his non-Jewish studies.

Two weeks after his interview with Father Zema,

however, Elijah was visited by a rough-looking gentile dressed in the garb of a church servant.

"I have a letter for the boy Elijah," he announced.

The rabbis stood by as the missive was handed him. The servitor smiled, bowed clumsily, and departed.

"My dear young friend," read the letter: "I have received word from the nuncio that I shall soon be elevated to a bishopric. I am convinced that this advancement has come as a result of the letter you advised me on. I was complimented on it. Accept my gratitude, and be assured that I shall always be glad to help you should the occasion arise."

It was signed by Father Zema.

The three forgot all their qualms in joy over this happy ending of the relationship between the boy and the priest. But suddenly Elijah felt giddy and fell into a chair.

"What is wrong? What has happened?" exclaimed Rabbi David.

And Elijah fearfully explained that he had just recalled the messenger as being one of the two men who had tried to kidnap him almost three years before —this being the one called Stasz.

9

FRIENDS AND PARENTS

The close watch on the boy Elijah was resumed. Everyone was convinced that there was some skullduggery in the air, that there were designs on the young student's freedom.

But among the townspeople all kinds of rumors were rife. Many had seen the boy with the priest, and were ready to believe anything. Young Jews remained away from institutions that were always hostile to Judaism, unless something untoward was in the offing. Even if the boy had only gone there to obtain some secular instruction, and that with his teacher, why should he even find the need to study his matters not in Sacred Writ? With far less incentive children had grown up to be apostates who, though they might not have adopted another religion, had little use for the teachings of their youth. The situation required much shaking of heads.

Elijah took no note of the whispers. He continued his studies as before, with no apparent further interest in any church functionary. And his fame spread, bringing the customary hosts of eager matchmakers.

"If this boy," urged one of these gentry upon Rabbi David, "becomes engaged to the daughter of the leading Jew in Kobrin, he will be rich, happy, will never have to do ordinary work, will have a beautiful wife of excellent family, and what is more—myself and my family will never want for anything any more. It is a righteous command to assist a needy family like mine!"

During three years away from home Elijah had been visited by his parents a half dozen times. They stayed for a short while only, and left tearfully though pridefully. The matchmakers were always put off until the father and mother should reach Kaidan again; but since no date was set the brokers were fortunately absent from the city on every such occasion.

Another happy visitation at this time was the coming of Rabbi Abraham Katzenellenbogen, accompanied by the brothers Mordecai and Asher.

Elijah was entering the house when he turned and saw the carriage pull up at the door. A dusty lad leaped out and embraced him, before he recognized the greatly grown Asher.

"You are so big!" cried Elijah, happily measuring the dimensions of his playmate of Brest-Litovsk.

"Of course I am big!" replied Asher. "I was Bar Mitzvah a week ago, and the family said that a thirteen-year-old is man enough to travel even so far as Kaidan. And you're not as little as you were, either!"

"No, that you aren't!" here broke in Mordecai, the bridegroom who had traveled with Elijah on his first journey out of Wilna.

Elijah took the young man's hand and enquired whether Esther, the wife, had not come along also.

"Oh, she cannot!" returned Mordecai. "Who would take care of our two little boys?"

"The older one calls me uncle already," smiled Asher.

Rabbi Abraham had completed his directions to the driver, and he too now greeted Elijah.

"I hear you have ceased studying Judaism!" he laughed.

"You hear wrongly," said Elijah, soberly. "Every time I look at a book not in Hebrew or on a scientific subject, someone thinks my world is coming to an end."

"Well," rejoined Abraham, "we ought to know something, at least, about the Creation on which we are living."

"That is what I think, and I am going to know everything!"

"Your life may be too short for everything."

"By that I mean I intend to study other subjects besides those Rabbi Moses gives me."

"What do you want to take up next?"

"Anatomy and medicine. I think everybody who can should learn how to heal his fellowman."

"But that will take so much of your time you will have no further opportunity to study with Rabbi Moses."

"I shall find time. It is important."

A number of elder townsfolk, gathered about, had heard the conversation. There was more shaking of heads.

"He will become a doctor and a *goy!* He will forget everything!" sorrowed one greybeard, while others nodded in dismay.

Thus, while Elijah happily disported himself with Asher, tongues once more were wagging about the wonder-child's unfortunate propensity for straying from the reservation of Torah and Talmud. The coachdriver hearkened with alarm as various mouths announced that now Elijah was venturing to give up everything he had thus far learnt in order to become a Godless physician. He determined that a warning would have to be transmitted to Wilna.

Asher, in the Katzenellenbogen home, was pleased to display his talmudic knowledge to his younger friend, and to receive encomia on his excellent advancement. His brother, who remained as a guest for two days, employed his time for business ends and then declared himself prepared to return to Brest-Litovsk. But Asher's plea that he be 'permitted to remain longer was seconded by the old pair, who welcomed the advent of a playmate for their charge.

At this time also a welcome visitor in the household was a scholar of Kaidan named Judah. R. Judah sometimes brought along his little girl Hannah, who was a favorite of the *rebbetzin*. To the credit of the father he never spoke of his daughter as a possible bride for the much sought after Elijah. And since he was the exception in this regard, it may be well to record here that when Elijah became eighteen he was to take to wife this very Hannah, daughter of Judah.

The boys often studied together under the tutelage of Rabbi Moses Margolis. This was a pleasant change for both students and instructor, and presented an opportunity for the kind of discussion afforded all who occupied themselves with talmudic lore.

Then one day came the most important of visitors. The parents of Elijah arrived from Wilna without warning. The boy saw them alighting from the coach, and ran from his seat near the window to embrace them in profound joy.

110

"Thank the Lord," began the father, "that you are safe, my son!"

"No harm has come to you, praise God!" repeated the mother.

"What could have happened to me?" asked Elijah. "I am secure here. I study and have friends and—"

"We have heard many rumors," interposed Solomon.

"Father," returned the boy, "all parents worry about their children, and if they do not hear rumors they create them."

"That may be true, but they say you are turning away from Jewish studies and going after the ways of the gentiles."

"You know I would not do that, father."

"Even though such statements are unbelievable, we wanted to see you to relieve our minds."

"Wouldn't you want to see me anyway, father?"

"Yes, my dear lad, but we have much to ask you."

"Let us come in to the rabbi."

Once seated in the living room of the Katzenellenbogens, Solomon the father entered more closely into his questioning.

"All these additional studies, that are so unnecessary for a Jew— are you certain that they do not take from your regular hours of Jewish study?"

"Rabbi Moses will tell you they do not."

The rabbi appealed to nodded and explained, "There is a limit to what I, his teacher, can teach him, but he can study every walking moment. He has time for other things. And what harm is there in a talmudic student

111

being better able to understand the figures, the vegetation, and the other special teachings of the Talmud?"

"Do you mean," asked Solomon, "that these other subjects are actually helpful in his Jewish learning?"

Rabbi Moses nodded once more.

"Then that is all right," smiled the father. "But I have heard news that is different—that Elijah is talking seriously of becoming a physician."

The boy was amazed that even this rumor should have reached Wilna.

"Is it not proper for a Jew to study medicine?" he asked. "And how do you know I thought of it?"

"Many people are interested in your progress," was the response, " and they talk of you everywhere. As to medicine, I do not see how you, a talmudic student, can undertake it."

"Maimonides and many other of our ancestors were great physicians."

"Yes, and when Maimonides practiced medicine, he himself writes that he had to neglect his other scholarly work."

"Yet he wrote much, father."

"He might have written more. It is enough that he complained. We have dedicated you to Judaism alone. To study medicine you must spend years over books and in practice. You may forget the Torah; you may some day, even though to you it seems impossible, forsake the Torah. We cannot give our consent."

"I shall obey you, of course," returned Elijah, sadly. "But I have already studied a book on anatomy. Here it is!"

He brought the large volume down from a shelf and handed it over to Rabbi Moses.

"I am finished with it," he said.

"And you will not forget it," stressed Rabbi Moses, thus intimating to the parents that their son could not ever fail to remember anything that once he had learnt.

Elijah then asked questions about his friends and aquaintances of Wilna, whom he had not seen for three years. This information was given him, and then he asked what had become of the pair who had by accident saved him from the kidnapers.

"Ezekiel Batlan and Shprintze?" Solomon laughed. "Listen, everyone. Since they decided to be more affectionate to each other a remarkable change has taken place. Ezekiel is busy all day selling vegetables; you can hardly drag him away from the cart. But Shprintze, the energetic, devotes all her time in the marketplace and over fences gossiping and expressing opinions about everything under the sun."

"And does Ezekiel then pull her away by the ear?" asked Elijah.

"Never! He just approaches and says, 'Shprintze, my dear one, is it not time to come home for our evening meal?' And the woman stops whatever she has been doing and they go home together arm in arm."

"The greatest miracle," commented Rabbi David, "since the days of Moses before Pharaoh!"

There was room in the large house for the parents too. They stayed on for several days, accompanying their son everywhere. But Solomon soon remarked that they were always being followed.

"What is this?" he asked. "Are you so honored by

the townspeople and the students here that they must go with you everywhere you go?"

"Well, you see," began Rabbi Moses, who was then walking with them, "Elijah is so precious to us that we watch him all the time."

"I can understand," remonstrated Solomon, "that when people are traveling in the open road they must sometimes have protection against highwaymen. And once when we thought that the Church wanted to take him, we worried about Elijah. But here in this city, where he has lived in security and where there are always people about—wherein lies the necessity of a body-guard?"

"A Jew is never certain," said Moses.

"Tell me," persisted the father. "I must know everything that concerns this treasure of mine!"

Thus pressed, the boy and his teacher admitted that they had seen one of the men who had twice attempted to kidnap him, and that the man was working for the church in the city and could not readily be touched.

The parents, alarmed, compelled the party to retrace its steps to the home of the rabbi.

"We must take him with us at once," they cried. "We cannot leave our son where he is in such danger!"

Rabbi David attempted to quiet them.

"You will destroy all we have built up!" he protested. "The boy is already the genius of his age. If you take him away, from books and instructors and all, what will happen to him?"

"What will happen if he is stolen or killed?" exclaimed Solomon.

"You have just forbidden him to study medicine

114

because that might stand in the way of his better application to Jewish lore. It will be worse for his studies if you interrupt them now on insufficient grounds."

"Insufficient grounds?" repeated Solomon. "Danger to the life of a person invalidates the other laws of Judaism. We can do almost anything ordinarily forbidden to save a life."

"But I tell you," firmly continued the rabbi, "that he is in no danger any longer. The curate is a friend of the boy's and would not permit him to be injured. He knows that Elijah could never be compelled, let alone persuaded, to join his own church. The man we speak of must have reformed, or he would not be working for the priest instead of holding up travelers in the forest."

"I am still not convinced. Remember, we are parents. We are willing to send a child far from home so that he may study and become a distinguished sage in Israel. We are willing to sacrifice many things, but not his physical security. What could your students here do if armed men snatched the boy away in their presence? They would be shot. And how would I be certain that even if I paid any ransom they demanded of me, that the boy would be returned? You know, Rabbi Katzenellenbogen, the ways of the gentiles in Lithuania and all central Europe, when they go into the business of molesting Jewish children."

"I know all this," admitted the rabbi, "and still I have no fear for your son. Must those who seek to take Elijah stick to one purpose all their days? Are there not other means of making a dishonest living?"

The parents spoke quietly to each other, and then Solomon turned to reply.

115

"Rabbi," he said, "our hearts tell us one thing, and your words speak reasonably to us of the opposite. Let us wait over night, and then give you our decision without emotion or heat."

Elijah, who had already been disappointed once through a parental order, found himself saddened by his father's words. Much as he loved his people and the city of his birth, he felt himself already a part of Kaidan, and he had a growing urge to study there until there was not another sentence of Jewish lore to con by heart.

The evening meal found Asher equally mournful over the imminent departure of his beloved young friend. In the eyes of the old people there was the look of parents about to lose an only son to the army in war time. Rabbi Moses drummed with his fingers on the table incessantly.

In the morning the conference reconvened.

"Have you come to any decision?" asked Rabbi David, apprehensively.

"Our purpose," said Solomon, "is to take Elijah home."

The heads of all present drooped.

"Except," continued Solomon, "on certain conditions."

All heads came to attention.

"I understand," said the father, "that there were two wicked men involved in the efforts to steal my son, and from you. So long as I know they are at large, I shall not be satisfied."

"But," spoke David, "If they are so vindictive, they

116

would find Elijah in Wilna or wherever you brought him!"

"At least I shall have him under my own care. I cannot trust your unarmed students to protect him."

"Shall I speak to the priest and have him arrest or dismiss his servant? What do you suggest?"

"I suggest nothing. So long as I cannot feel secure about these ruffians, I must take Elijah back with me to Wilna."

Then came the almost miraculous event which Kaidan did not forget for many years. There was a loud scuffle just outside the door. There was silence for a moment, and then a singular company trooped in.

Two strangers in churchly work clothes appeared. Each was in the clutches of two determined students, while another held a poised club over his head.

"We found them waiting outside," volunteered another young man to the rabbi, "and we captured them. Are those the scoundrels you asked us to look out for?"

Elijah jumped from his seat to confront the prisoners.

"They are the ones!" he cried. "I remember them well! Their names are Stasz and Vanoff!"

End Of Danger

In the crowded study of Rabbi David Katzenellenbogen there took place a tableau never before known
in Kaidan.

Jews who had timidly suffered every indignity from
non-Jewish hoodlums turned the tables, and became
Maccabean heroes in their own right. Students with
backs bent through long sessions over heavy tomes now
stood like angels of vengeance, prepared to thrust and
parry and kill. The hostile looks in the eyes of all the Jews
present almost congealed the blood in the veins of the
captives.

For they had remotely heard in their youth that Jews
were cruel assassins who would never hesitate to shed
gentile blood. That they had never known of a case that
could fall into that category, and that they had more
than once themselves attempted to spill the blood of
Israelites did not expel the old false teaching from their
minds. The great hulking heroes, whose features seemed
to be all spreading nose, appeared to shrink momentarily,
until their proportions approximated those of the smaller Jews about them.

Elijah's parents had taken protective stands on either
side of him. Rabbi David sat behind his desk like a
judge ready to pronounce sentence. The rest, warders,

jury, prosecutors, spelled the apparent doom of the criminals at the bar.

The rabbi knew inwardly that all this was illegal. No Jew could be a policeman, let alone a judge. The servitors of the church were sacrosanct. Yet his love for Elijah was so great—coupled with his love for Israel, to be saved by its great men of scholarship— that he threw off all precautions in his conduct toward the gentiles.

"What were you doing about my house?" he demanded, in Polish.

But Stasz, fearsome, replied in Yiddish.

"We are doing no harm," he whined. "We were bringing a massage from our master."

"Does your master require two messengers?"

"I just went along," offered Vanoff, also in Yiddish.

"How is it," asked the rabbi, "that you use our language?"

Moses Margolis stepped forward to reply.

"These men must be the worst rascals in the community," he said. "We have such as these, who have picked up Yiddish, who come to synagogues pretending to be Jews. They generally obtain alms, but sometimes they come only to discover whom to rob or what slanders to bring to the authorities."

"You have us wrong," protested Stasz.

"Do you deny that these things are done?"

"We admit playing tricks like that," pleaded Stasz, "but we have no designs on Jews now."

"Did you not," Rabbi David resumed the examination, "at least twice attempt to kidnap the boy Elijah of Wilna?"

120

"We admit it," answered Stasz, the spokesman, "but that was long ago, and will never happen again."

"You cannot deny it. Anyone who has once seen you cannot fail to recognize you. Did anyone ask you to steal this boy today?"

"I tell you, rabbi, no. We both work for Father Zema. We have a place to sleep and enough to eat, and wear these fine clothes, which all the people respect. Why should we commit crimes and be hanged?"

"Does Father Zema know what you have been up to?"

"He sent me here!"

"For what purpose?"

"He has something to give the boy."

"Why didn't he send it with you?"

"He wishes to present it in person."

Here Vanoff veered about, and was met by two up-raised cudgels. He resumed his place next to Stasz, who pointed a finger at the rabbi.

"You dare not touch either of us!" he cried. "We are peaceful citizens who have done you no harm."

"And we," replied the rabbi, "are only Jews, who have no rights against even the lowest of gentiles. But the courts are just, and we can find witnesses, Jewish and gentile, of your attempt to kidnap the boy Elijah. We can have you in custody at any time we desire."

The pair grew panicky.

"But I tell you," insisted Stasz, "that we have chosen a different life. The father knows all about us, and will testify for us. Jews are not permitted to condemn anyone without giving the one accused every opportunity to offer his defense."

"You know something about Jewish law too," remarked the rabbi. "It is good to understand Yiddish and listen in to the discussions in the Jewish study halls. But if these young men had beaten you to death and then testified that you had made an attempt once more on this lad here, who would have failed to believe them?"

Vanoff, his knees buckling under him, raised his hand to indicate that he had valid testimony to offer.

"Call Father Zema," he urged. "He will tell you we are not lying to you."

"A good idea. Will two of you young men go to the church house? Tell the curate that his men have fallen into trouble, and that they have asked him to come to help them."

While a pair of students departed on this errand the tableau was resumed. The prisoners stood as before, threatened by fists and sticks, and facing an angry group of Jews, reinforced by a growing mob about the house. Not one of the Jews gave a thought to the punishment that might be his for venturing to apprehend and question two servants of the priest; their indignation left them no other course.

The room was becoming uncomfortably warm when Father Zema arrived in extraordinary haste.

"What has happened to my men?" he demanded, as he pushed his way into the room.

"Nothing has happened, good father," answered Rabbi David. "But these men were found about my house, and they were suspected of wishing to do harm to the boy Elijah, whom you know and have taught."

"You found both? I sent only one."

"But, father," spoke Vanoff, "I often go with Stasz,

and he goes with me. Besides, we were afraid something like this might happen."

"Why were you afraid?"

"You remember," Vanoff grew red and uncomfortable, "that in our full confession to you, we spoke of robberies and attempted kidnapings?"

A light dawned on the priest's features.

"And is it this boy Elijah that you tried to abduct?"

"Yes, father."

At this confession the group, previously fearful of reprisals for their extra-legal conduct, visibly relaxed. Rabbi David arose and addressed the priest.

"You see now, Father Zema, why we took these precautions. It is better so, for if I had not been here to examine these men, my young men might have done them great injury."

"I cannot blame you," declared the priest. "I know how precious this youth must be to you and all your people. I have seen the workings of his mind. But let me offer a defense of my two servants."

Additional chairs were brought in, permitting the priest and his men to be seated.

"Let me tell you the entire story," began Father Zema. "These men came to me several months ago, asking for bread. I fed them and then inquired when they had last been to mass and confession. They admitted having neglected their religious duties. Their appearance, as you see, was against them—of which I must speak again.

"They broke down under my questioning and admitted a long series of petty crimes, most of them against your people. There was no murder nor mayhem in the list. Their favorite act was to pose as Jews and get charity from your officials or sometimes execute a swindle. Then they bethought themselves of making a killing, that is, of stealing a rich man's son and holding him for ransom. All this they confessed to me.

"It was after their second failure that they gave up the idea of earning a livelihood in that manner. As a matter of fact, they have been here for many weeks and could have kidnaped the boy Elijah a hundred times. I did not know until now who had been the object of their criminality, but the very fact that they made no effort to reach him all this while is proof to me that they wished to live straight.

"I want to tell you one more thing. Often I have discussed the lives and careers of the men you hold here with themselves. When they were younger they were both injured in the face; and their peculiar noses turned people away from them. Even when they were given work, they were likely to be discharged in a day. They grew sourer every week, until they determined to gain a livelihood by their wits. Knowing Yiddish, it was easy for them to get money out of charitably minded Jews. But now that I have given them regular work in my house and church, there is no further reason for them to steal or commit worse crimes.

"I respect the youth Elijah, who has performed a greater favor for me than I ever for him. So far as I am concerned no harm will ever befall him. And can Stasz and Vanoff do him harm any longer? Most certainly not. Their previous crimes are known; their features cannot be concealed. Elijah is safe from them, and I hope from all evil men."

124

There were no cudgels in evidence now, nor were there further hostile glances directed toward the priest's men.

"I wish to thank you, Father Zema," said Rabbi David, "for honoring our community again with your presence, and for having settled our fears concerning the boy Elijah."

"I am honored," bowed the priest, "to be in the presence of so much learning. Though I hope to see all men in the fold of my faith, I can recognize knowledge and honest belief in everyone. I am sorry that so often do fellow priests and coreligionists speak ill of the people of Israel. We are all sons of the one God. As to Elijah, I feel certain that his name will be remembered on earth when my own is utterly forgotten."

The boy's parents beamed. Never had their son been so immoderately praised, and by a priest of the ruling religion. They bowed their thanks to Father Zema.

"These are the parents," explained Rabbi David, "now visiting in our city. They were intending to remove the lad from Kaidan, on the ground that he was not safe here; but now that you have spoken, I am certain that they will not carry out that intention."

"We will not," assented Solomon.

Here the priest drew a book from the fold of his cassock. He held it toward Elijah.

"Son," he said, "you have proved yourself a scholar in other things besides religious learning. And since I am indebted to you, I have decided to offer you books which can help in your added studies. Here is a late book on mathematics by a great German philosopher, Gottfried Wilhelm Leibnitz, who died less than twenty years

125

ago. It is yours and there will be more for you in the days to come. It is about this gift that I summoned you through this unfortunate Mister Stasz."

Elijah happily accepted the gift, and Father Zema shook his hand with every evidence of kindly friendship.

The priest spoke again.

"And lest you have other fears," he addressed the parents, "I promise that I shall give Elijah no book on my faith or that may disturb his religious beliefs. Let him remain an honor to his race. We shall find others to save and bring to Mother Church."

A shout of approval came from the students, who had never before heard so tolerant and friendly a speech from an official of the Church. To some, who had sufered mentally under the lash of a dominant faith that forever demanded their immediate conversion, this was almost the sign of the millenium. Every face reflected a suddenly found happiness.

The color had returned to the faces of Stasz and Vanoff.

"Father," said the latter, "I am sorry that I caused all this trouble by going along when you had given the order to Stasz. Shall we go now?"

"My sons," spoke the priest, "you see now that sinning brings but to death. Your early misdeeds sought you out. But I was here to redeem you from destruction."

"Father," said Stasz, "may I speak?"

"Say what you will."

"We two wish to apologize to all those we have injured, and in particular to the boy Elijah. We know we have been wicked men, and understand the pain we would have caused his parents, who are here, if we had carried

126

out our plot. We respect the boy more and more, as we have heard what the world thinks of him. We ask his forgiveness."

And suddenly the two ruffianly servitors dropped to their knees and kissed the hands of the astonished lad.

Then Stasz arose and continued.

"Not only will we do you no harm, Master Elijah, but we shall be glad to take over the task of these brave students. We promise to watch over you whenever the opportunity comes. Let us prove that we are loyal members of our Church, and let this be our good deed in its name."

The assembly departed from the house in unusually jovial spirits. As Father Zema started toward his own home, he had an honor escort of fifty pious Jews; while Stasz and Vanoff, already beginning their self-appointed task, hovered over little Elijah like protective angels—with the features of devils!

Elijah Gaon of Wilna did not return to his home city until he reached the age of twenty-five. In that year both Stasz and Vanoff, faithful friends of the Jew they had once sought to injure, both passed from this earth.

Elijah was married to Hanna, daughter of R. Judah, as related, when he was eighteen. He continued his studies, being supported in the household of his father-in-law. In 1750, when he was thirty, he received a small legacy in the form of a welcome weekly allowance.

A modest man, the Gaon was frequently consulted on controversies in high places among his people. He always refused to accept the position of active rabbi, but he was accepted as the spiritual head not alone of Wilna but of all Lithuanian and Russian Jewry.

Among Elijah's achievements of later years were improvements in the conduct of synagogue services, greater humaneness in the giving of charity, and a halt to the spread of Hassidism, which in his time threatened to engulf all Jewry in a flood of kabbalistic mysticism.

When he died in 1797, Jews everywhere mourned the passing of Israel's greatest intellectual and spiritual guide of modern times. Nor has his successor yet appeared among us.

Elijah was the author of seventy works, all written before he was forty. He composed commentaries on the Bible; treatises on biblical geography, chronology, and archaeology; commentaries on the talmudic literature of Jerusalem, as well as on the Babylonian Talmud and all the Midrashim or sermonic works on Jewish lore; full comments on the best known books of Kabbalah; textbooks of astronomy, algebra, and trigonometry; a grammar of the Hebrew language; and the outstandingly important commentary on the great code of Jewish law, the Shulhan Arukh.

The effect of the Gaon's ideas on later Jewish studies was tremendous. He opposed the extreme involvement of argument that too many talmudists engaged in. He insisted that interpretation of the Talmud must be based on reason and not merely on authority. He saw that many doubtful texts were corrected. He combined all that was good in ancient and medieval Jewish thought with all that was of worth in modern modes of thinking. Though always repudiating the appellation, he was properly called Elijah the Saint, a leader bent not alone on perfecting his own character, but on improving the soul of every member of his people.

Great is a people that can produce such men. May his counterpart yet appear in the parlous age through which Israel is passing!